ENERGY SCIENCE, ENGINEERING AND TECHNOLOGY

INNOVATIONS IN ENERGY

EFFICIENT TECHNOLOGIES FOR BUILDINGS

ENERGY SCIENCE, ENGINEERING AND TECHNOLOGY

Additional books in this series can be found on Nova's website under the Series tab.

Additional E-books in this series can be found on Nova's website under the E-book tab.

ENERGY SCIENCE, ENGINEERING AND TECHNOLOGY

INNOVATIONS IN ENERGY

EFFICIENT TECHNOLOGIES FOR BUILDINGS

DAVID I. MATTHEWS
EDITOR

Nova Science Publishers, Inc.
New York

NOTICE TO THE READER

The Publisher has taken reasonable care in the preparation of this book, but makes no expressed or implied warranty of any kind and assumes no responsibility for any errors or omissions. No liability is assumed for incidental or consequential damages in connection with or arising out of information contained in this book. The Publisher shall not be liable for any special, consequential, or exemplary damages resulting, in whole or in part, from the readers' use of, or reliance upon, this material. Any parts of this book based on government reports are so indicated and copyright is claimed for those parts to the extent applicable to compilations of such works.

Independent verification should be sought for any data, advice or recommendations contained in this book. In addition, no responsibility is assumed by the publisher for any injury and/or damage to persons or property arising from any methods, products, instructions, ideas or otherwise contained in this publication.

This publication is designed to provide accurate and authoritative information with regard to the subject matter covered herein. It is sold with the clear understanding that the Publisher is not engaged in rendering legal or any other professional services. If legal or any other expert assistance is required, the services of a competent person should be sought. FROM A DECLARATION OF PARTICIPANTS JOINTLY ADOPTED BY A COMMITTEE OF THE AMERICAN BAR ASSOCIATION AND A COMMITTEE OF PUBLISHERS.
Additional color graphics may be available in the e-book version of this book.

LIBRARY OF CONGRESS CATALOGING-IN-PUBLICATION DATA

Innovations in energy : efficient technologies for buildings / editor, David I. Matthews.
    p. cm.
  Publications from the Office of Energy Efficiency and Renewable Energy (EERE) at the U.S. Department of Energy.
  Includes index.
  ISBN 978-1-61761-976-2 (hardcover)
  1. Buildings--Energy conservation. 2. Building fittings. I. Matthews, David I. II. United States. Dept. of Energy. Office of Energy Efficiency and Renewable Energy.
  TJ163.5.B84I56 2012
  696--dc23

2011052253

Published by Nova Science Publishers, Inc. ✛ *New York*

CONTENTS

PREFACE

Today's buildings consume more energy than any other sector of the U.S. economy, including transportation and industry. The Energy Information Administration (EIA) estimates that energy consumption in buildings will exceed 50 quads in the next two decades. Investment in energy efficiency research and development (R&D) within the buildings sector could significantly reduce energy consumption. This book discusses the building technologies program, as well as technologies and products supported by them.

Chapter 1 - Today's buildings consume more energy than any other sector of the U.S. economy, including transportation and industry. In 2006, it took approximately 39 quadrillion Btu (quads) of energy to service the 113 million households and 74.8 billion square feet of commercial floor space in the United States—almost 39% of total U.S. energy consumption. And as the U.S. population grows and the economy shifts and expands, the demand for energy will only increase. The Energy Information Administration (EIA) estimates that energy consumption in buildings—primarily electricity and natural gas—will exceed 50 quads in the next two decades.

Investment in energy efficiency research and development (R&D) within the buildings sector could significantly reduce energy consumption. But private-sector R&D has been minimal at best, largely because of the different types of firms that construct or operate buildings (e.g., manufacturers, designers, builders, subcontractors, and suppliers). Because their business goals and priorities are so varied, their abilities or incentives to build cost-effective, energy efficient buildings are limited.

Chapter 2 - The purpose of the project described in this report is to identify and characterize commercially available products and emerging (near-commercial) technologies that benefited from the support of the Building

Technologies Program (BTP) within the U.S. Department of Energy's Office of Energy Efficiency and Renewable Energy. The investigation specifically focused on technology-oriented research and development (R&D) projects sponsored by BTP's Emerging Technologies subprogram from 2005-2009.

To perform this analysis, Pacific Northwest National Laboratory (PNNL) investigated 190 technology R&D projects funded directly by the Emerging Technologies subprogram or via the Small Business Innovation Research and Small Business Technology Transfer programs. This effort identified 11 commercially available products, 41 emerging technologies, and 68 "potential" technologies that are still being researched but are more than three years away from commercialization. These technologies were grouped according to the four major R&D areas of the Emerging Technologies subprogram: envelope, HVAC and water heating, lighting, and windows. The lighting R&D area accounted for the majority of all technologies identified in this study, including 58% of all commercially available and emerging technologies and 69% of all potential technologies. These findings are consistent with the fact that more than 50% of the Emerging Technologies subprogram's total budget during 2005-2009 was allocated to lighting R&D, with most lighting R&D funding occurring from 2007-2009. In addition, many of the activities conducted in the envelope and windows areas advance the development of energy-efficient buildings through mechanisms other than new commercial products.

In: Innovations in Energy
Editor: David I. Matthews

ISBN: 978-1-61761-976-2
© 2012 Nova Science Publishers, Inc.

Chapter 1

BUILDING TECHNOLOGIES PROGRAM OVERVIEW[*]

The Office of Energy Efficiency and Renewable Energy (EERE) at the United States Department of Energy

INTRODUCTION

Today's buildings consume more energy than any other sector of the U.S. economy, including transportation and industry. In 2006, it took approximately 39 quadrillion Btu (quads) of energy to service the 113 million households and 74.8 billion square feet of commercial floor space in the United States—almost 39% of total U.S. energy consumption.[1] And as the U.S. population grows and the economy shifts and expands, the demand for energy will only increase. The Energy Information Administration (EIA) estimates that energy consumption in buildings—primarily electricity and natural gas— will exceed 50 quads in the next two decades.[2]

Investment in energy efficiency research and development (R&D) within the buildings sector could significantly reduce energy consumption. But private-sector R&D has been minimal at best, largely because of the different types of firms that construct or operate buildings (e.g., manufacturers,

---

[*] This is an edited, reformatted and augmented version of The Office of Energy Efficiency and Renewable Energy (EERE) at the U.S. Department of Energy. A link to this Overview can be found at the following Building Technologies Program website: http://www1.eere. energy.gov/ buildings/ plans_ implementation_results.html (viewed November 2011).

designers, builders, subcontractors, and suppliers). Because their business goals and priorities are so varied, their abilities or incentives to build cost-effective, energy efficient buildings are limited.

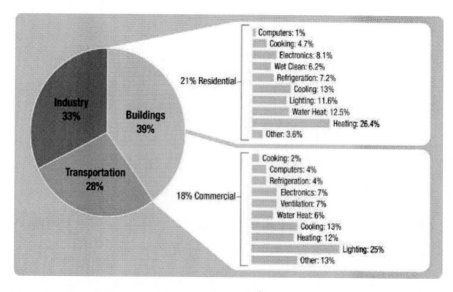

Figure 1. U.S. primary energy consumption, 2006[3].

As the lead federal agency responsible for increasing energy efficiency and reducing carbon emissions in the buildings sector, the Building Technologies Program (BTP) is working in collaboration with the private sector, funding research, development, and demonstration (RD&D) activities through public–private partnerships. In addition to helping industry partners develop the techniques and strategies for implementing today's energy efficient building technologies, the program funds high-risk, precompetitive research in the early phases of development. As activities progress from developing technology to validating technical goals, the government's cost share will diminish as private industries and institutions begin to take on the costs. BTP helps to bring technologies to the point where the private sector can successfully integrate them into buildings and the commercial market.

In addition to compensating for the obstacles to private-sector investment in building R&D, BTP plays a regulatory role in protecting consumers from products that utilize costly amounts of energy or harm the environment as a result of their use. The program establishes efficiency standards for energy-consuming equipment used in residential and commercial buildings under the authority of the Energy Policy and Conservation Act of 1975, as amended.

Program representatives also assist in devising and promulgating building codes—targeting energy conservation—that fall under state and local jurisdiction.

PROGRAM MISSION, GOALS, AND OBJECTIVES

To support national goals of greater energy independence and a cleaner environment, BTP embraces its mission to develop technologies, techniques, and tools for making residential and commercial buildings more energy efficient, productive, and affordable. BTP researchers carry out the program's mission by working to improve the energy efficiency of individual building components, equipment, and integrated whole-building systems. In addition, they explore ways to integrate renewable energy systems into building design and operation and to accelerate the adoption of these technologies and practices.

BTP's long-term strategic goal is to create technologies and design approaches that lead to marketable zero energy homes (ZEHs) by 2020 and zero-energy commercial buildings (ZEBs) by 2025. A net-zero-energy building requires significantly less energy because of efficiency gains (60% to 70% less than a conventional building), with the balance of energy requirements supplied by renewable technologies. These efficiency gains also find application in buildings currently being constructed, resulting in immediate energy savings.

APPROACHES TO ACHIEVING ENERGY EFFICIENCY GOALS

The program takes a three-pronged approach, described in the sections that follow and illustrated in Figure 2. The overall goal is to propel the buildings sector toward more energy efficient buildings that also incorporate renewable power technologies.

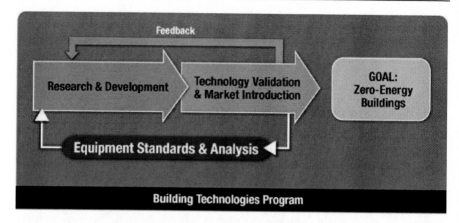

Figure 2. How the three areas work together toward the zero-energy goals[5].

RESEARCH AND DEVELOPMENT

BTP's residential buildings R&D efforts focus on improving the efficiency of the approximately 1.5 to 2 million new homes built each year in the United States, as well as the more than 100 million homes that already exist. The program has two major residential building R&D targets: (1) developing climate-specific and cost-effective technology packages that achieve an average 40% reduction in whole house energy use by 2010, and (2) developing technologies and solutions that lead to a 70% reduction in energy use in new homes by 2020.

On the commercial buildings front, BTP researchers are exploring energy savings opportunities in new and existing commercial buildings. In collaboration with industry, BTP will develop, document, and disseminate technology packages to help builders reduce energy use by 30% in new, small- to medium-sized commercial buildings by 2010. Program researchers are also developing a set of initial technology options as a basis for achieving a 50% energy use reduction in commercial buildings.

Finally, BTP researchers are working to accelerate the development and integration of technologies for new and advanced lighting, building envelopes, windows, space conditioning, water heating, and appliances.

EQUIPMENT STANDARDS, GUIDELINES, AND ANALYSES

BTP's standards subprogram conducts activities in three specific areas: test procedures, mandatory energy conservation standards, and labeling.

To improve the efficiency of appliances and equipment, program researchers conduct analyses and develop national standards that are technologically feasible and economically justified. Such codes, standards, and guidelines can increase the minimum efficiency levels of integrated building systems and save significant amounts of energy. By 2010, BTP will issue several formal proposals for enhanced product standards and test procedures.

TECHNOLOGY VALIDATION AND MARKET INTRODUCTION

BTP administers several programs designed to accelerate the adoption of energy efficient and renewable energy technologies, including EnergySmart Schools, EnergySmart Hospitals, Building Energy Codes, and the Solar Decathlon.

BTP's **EnergySmart Hospitals** and **EnergySmart Schools** programs are helping health care and educational institutions put funds previously spent on energy into patient care and school improvements. The nation's 8,000 hospitals are among our most complex, diverse, and energy-intensive facilities, spending more than $5 billion a year on energy and producing approximately 30 pounds of carbon dioxide (CO_2) emissions per square foot.[6] Clearly, there's much room for improvement in hospital energy use. And schools spend more on energy than any other expense except personnel. High-performance, energy efficient schools can lower a school district's operating costs by as much as 30%, without sacrificing educational quality.[7]

In support of the Energy Conservation and Production Act, Section 304, BTP's Building Energy Codes segment offers technical and financial assistance to states to update and implement their energy codes and boost the construction of more energy efficient buildings.

BTP also sponsors the Solar Decathlon, a high-profile university competition held biannually on the National Mall in Washington, D.C. The competition showcases highly efficient building technologies, ZEHs, and almost all forms of renewable energy. BTP invests in innovations highlighted during the competition, ranging from energy efficient, whole-building design approaches, through advanced window and building envelope technologies, to heating and cooling equipment, appliances, and lights.

In addition, BTP partners with the Environmental Protection Agency on ENERGY STAR® activities to remove technical, financial, and institutional barriers to the widespread awareness, availability, and purchase of highly efficient appliances, compact fluorescent lighting (CFL) products, windows, and other new or advanced products. For example, BTP has targeted increasing the market share of ENERGY STAR windows to 65% by 2010 and maintaining the 28% market share for ENERGY STAR appliances.

BTP RESEARCH TEAM AND PARTNERS

For **residential buildings**, BTP sponsors **Building America**, an industry-driven research program aimed at accelerating the development and adoption of ZEH technologies in new and existing homes. Building America research teams, made up of key members of the building industry involved in the production of advanced residential buildings, conduct systems engineering research to develop technologies and strategies to construct homes— on a community scale— that use 40% to 100% less source energy. The teams include:

- The **Building America Industrialized Housing Partnership (BAIHP)** collaborates with factory builders, affordable housing providers, and other builder partners primarily in the Southeast and the Northwest.
- The **Building Industry Research Alliance (BIRA)**, which operates primarily on the West Coast, consists of more than 80 industry partners representing a wide variety of builders, architects, manufacturers, state energy offices, utilities, and representatives from all aspects of the new residential homebuilding industry.
- The **Building Science Consortium (BSC)** members are helping in the construction of energy and resource efficient homes and communities that sustain affordable, high-quality living environments.
- The **Consortium for Advanced Residential Buildings (CARB)** works with scores of professionals throughout the homebuilding industry to design, engineer, and test affordable high-performance homes.

- **Integrated Building and Construction Solutions (IBACOS)** partners with innovative builders and developers to deliver homes that are more energy-efficient, safe, healthy, durable, comfortable, and environmentally responsible.
- The **National Association of Home Builders Research Center (NAHBRC)**, a subsidiary of the National Association of Home Builders, promotes innovation in housing technology to improve the durability, affordability, and environmental performance of homes and building products.

For **commercial buildings**, BTP's Net-Zero Energy **Commercial Building Initiative (CBI)** is aggressively working to improve the performance and decrease the energy consumption of commercial buildings. To help set research priorities and offer advice based on real-world implementation, industry representatives are heavily involved in the initiative through two activities, **Commercial Building Partnerships (CBP)** and **Commercial Building Energy Alliances (CBEAs)**. The CBPs are companies and organizations selected by BTP representatives to conduct cost-shared research, development, and deployment of advanced buildings technologies. The CBPs are charged with constructing buildings that achieve savings of 50% or retrofitting buildings to achieve 30% savings above the ASHRAE/IESNA Standard 90.1-2004.[8]

The CBEAs are a more informal group of organizations that play key roles in transforming the energy efficiency of commercial buildings. These alliances, including the **Retailer Energy Alliance, Commercial Real Estate Energy Alliance**, and **Hospital Energy Alliance**, serve as a compelling voice on the collective demand for highly efficient commercial buildings products and services.

BTP ACTIVITIES AND ACCOMPLISHMENTS

BTP has made great strides in speeding the market adoption of today's proven energy efficient technologies and researching new technologies that are reducing costs and increasing the performance of the nation's buildings. Homes being built today using the best practices developed through BTP's Building America research program are capable of decreasing the energy used in comparable new homes by as much as 40%. Compact fluorescent lamps

(CFLs) have captured more than 20% of the lighting market, thanks in large part to ENERGY STAR promotions. Additional success stories follow:

- The program's EnergyPlus software allows commercial building designers to calculate the savings potential of a wide range of energy options and combinations. The software was recognized with an R&D 100 Award as one of the 100 most technologically significant new products of 2003. Since 2001, more than 66,000 copies have been downloaded.

- In 2004, the program's solid state lighting researchers also garnered an R&D 100 Award for the development of a new process for growing gallium nitride on an etched sapphire substrate. The process, called cantilever epitaxy, promises to make brighter and more efficient green, blue, and white light-emitting diodes (LEDs).

- During the past 12 years, BTP has established technical compliance criteria for achieving the ENERGY STAR labels on washing machines, dishwashers, refrigerators, room air conditioners, freezers, windows, doors and skylights, solid state lighting luminaries, and domestic hot water heaters in addition to CFLs.

- BTP is enlisting the homebuilding industry to construct more energy efficient homes through the Builders Challenge initiative. The Builders Challenge offers information and strategies to help move the residential market toward the net-zero energy goals.

- Through an aggressive EnergySmart Hospitals program that combines conservation, efficiency, and renewable energy, Gundersen Lutheran Health System—a nonprofit serving the tri-state region of western Wisconsin, northeastern Iowa, and southeastern Minnesota—is realizing its goals of reducing baseline energy costs by 20% by the end of 2009 and achieving 100% energy neutrality by 2014.

- As part of the EnergySmart Schools program, Fossil Ridge High School in Fort Collins, Colorado, was able to reduce its energy costs by $153,000 without added costs for design or construction.

- After a tornado destroyed or damaged 95% of the homes and businesses in Greensburg, Kansas, on May 4, 2007, the city is rebuilding as a model green community with the help of BTP and other DOE personnel. The city's master rebuilding plan includes reducing energy use in buildings; seeking LEED Platinum ratings for new city building projects; and incorporating biodiesel, solar, and wind power systems into its community systems.

- The ENERGY STAR Operation Change Out military challenge, a joint effort between DOE and the U.S. Department of Defense, is the first national energy efficiency campaign focused on the military. The challenge encourages every serviceman and woman to save energy and money and protect the environment by replacing their inefficient, incandescent light bulbs with ENERGY STAR qualified bulbs. From the campaign's launch on Earth Day in 2008 through early June 2009, 151 bases had signed up, collectively changing out nearly 848,800 light bulbs. Over the lifetime of the bulbs, these change-outs are estimated to save more than 239 million kilowatt-hours, cut nearly $25.4 million in energy costs, and prevent nearly 382 million pounds of CO_2 emissions.

End Notes

[1] http://buildingsdatabook.eren.doe.gov/ChapterView.aspx?chap=1#1, accessed August 2009.
[2] http://apps1.eere.energy
    accessed August 2009.
[3] Buildings Energy Data Book http://buildingsdatabook.eren.doe.gov/
[5] http://www1.eere.energy accessed August 2009.
[6] http://www1.eere.energy accessed August 2009.
[7] http://www1.eere.energy accessed August 2009.
[8] http://www.energycodes.gov/training accessed August 2009.

In: Innovations in Energy
Editor: David I. Matthews

ISBN: 978-1-61761-976-2
© 2012 Nova Science Publishers, Inc.

Chapter 2

BUILDINGS R&D BREAKTHROUGHS: TECHNOLOGIES AND PRODUCTS SUPPORTED BY THE BUILDING TECHNOLOGIES PROGRAM[*]

United States Department of Energy Energy Efficiency and Renewable Energy Building Technologies Program

EXECUTIVE SUMMARY

The purpose of the project described in this report is to identify and characterize commercially available products and emerging (near-commercial) technologies that benefited from the support of the Building Technologies Program (BTP) within the U.S. Department of Energy's Office of Energy Efficiency and Renewable Energy. The investigation specifically focused on technology-oriented research and development (R&D) projects sponsored by BTP's Emerging Technologies subprogram from 2005-2009.

To perform this analysis, Pacific Northwest National Laboratory (PNNL) investigated 190 technology R&D projects funded directly by

---

[*] This is an edited, reformatted and augmented version of the U.S. Department of Energy publication, Energy Efficiency and Renewable Energy; Building Technologies Program, dated May 2011.

the Emerging Technologies subprogram or via the Small Business Innovation Research and Small Business Technology Transfer programs. This effort identified 11 commercially available products, 41 emerging technologies, and 68 "potential" technologies that are still being researched but are more than three years away from commercialization. These technologies were grouped according to the four major R&D areas of the Emerging Technologies subprogram: envelope, HVAC and water heating, lighting, and windows. The lighting R&D area accounted for the majority of all technologies identified in this study, including 58% of all commercially available and emerging technologies and 69% of all potential technologies. These findings are consistent with the fact that more than 50% of the Emerging Technologies subprogram's total budget during 2005-2009 was allocated to lighting R&D, with most lighting R&D funding occurring from 2007-2009. In addition, many of the activities conducted in the envelope and windows areas advance the development of energy-efficient buildings through mechanisms other than new commercial products.

Three types of organizations received grants to develop these building technologies: private companies, universities, and national laboratories. Private companies accounted for 73% of commercially available and emerging technologies and 56% of potential technologies. Universities had a much more prominent representation among potential technologies (25%) than commercially available/emerging technologies (11.5%), while national laboratories had an almost identical representation (15-19%) among both groups.

Where possible, PNNL also quantified the energy savings' and emissions' reductions benefits resulting from using commercially available technologies that are more energy efficient than the established baseline technologies they were designed to replace. These results are presented on a per-technology basis as part of a set of detailed descriptions that was developed for each commercially available and emerging technology.

This report documents the methodology and results of PNNL's technology tracking effort, including various analytical cross-sections and descriptions of the commercially available and emerging technologies that resulted from support of the Emerging Technologies subprogram from 2005-2009.

1.0. INTRODUCTION

This report documents the methodology and results of an effort to identify and characterize commercially available products and emerging[1] technologies that benefited from the support of the Building Technologies Program (BTP) within the U.S. Department of Energy's (DOE's) Office of Energy Efficiency and Renewable Energy (EERE). The investigation specifically focused on technology-oriented research and development (R&D) projects sponsored by BTP's Emerging Technologies subprogram from 2005-2009. Pacific Northwest National Laboratory (PNNL) has been conducting similar technology tracking activities for EERE's Industrial Technologies Program (and its predecessors) for more than 20 years and for EERE's Fuel Cell Technologies Program since FY 2008.

Commercialization of technologies that were developed in a government R&D program is generally viewed as an indicator of that program's success. The information presented in this report on commercially available and emerging technologies therefore fulfills the initial objectives of assessing BTP's technology R&D efforts during 2005-2009 and identifying technologies that are close to entering the commercial marketplace. With the long-term tracking of commercialization successes, BTP is more likely to effectively manage its R&D programs, repeat successful approaches to commercialization, and learn from unsuccessful attempts. The full intent of the PNNL effort is to periodically provide BTP with an updated report, thereby continually capturing the energy savings and other benefits of new BTP-funded technologies as they transition from R&D to the marketplace.

To provide some context, this chapter presents an overview of BTP's organization and core program areas, including the relationship of the Emerging Technologies subprogram to the rest of BTP. The chapter concludes with a brief summary of the information appearing within the remaining chapters and appendices of this report.

1.1. Organization of BTP and the Emerging Technologies Subprogram

The BTP is tasked with increasing energy efficiency and decreasing carbon emissions in the buildings sector of the U.S. economy. The Program's vision is to "significantly improve the efficiency of existing and new buildings through the development of conservation technologies, strategies, and practices."[2] To achieve this vision, BTP works with private companies, national laboratories, universities, and other government agencies to conduct research, development, demonstration, and deployment activities aimed at carrying out its mission: "to develop technologies, techniques, and tools for making residential and commercial buildings more energy efficient, productive, and affordable."[2]

The Program is divided into three primary areas: R&D, equipment standards and analysis, and technology validation and market introduction. The development of new, energy-efficient technologies falls under the scope of the R&D group, which is divided into three subprograms: Residential Buildings Integration, Commercial Buildings Integration, and Emerging Technologies. The Emerging Technologies subprogram is responsible for carrying out R&D and technology transfer activities associated with energy-efficient products and technologies for residential and commercial buildings.[3] Projects funded by this subprogram were therefore the focus of the technology tracking efforts presented in this report.

The major technology-oriented research thrusts of the Emerging Technologies subprogram are summarized below. Each focus area represents a specific group of technologies that can be combined with the other groups to achieve BTP's goal of cost-effective, energy-efficient commercial buildings and homes.

Envelope

Building envelope R&D contributes to BTP goals by developing new materials, systems, and designs that reduce energy losses through a building's outer surfaces. One important focus of this R&D work is the development of a next-generation attic/roof system that will reduce energy losses by 50% compared with the Building America baseline. In pursuit of this goal, BTP sponsors the development and integration of key individual envelope technologies, including cool roofs, thermal mass technologies, radiant barriers, and above-deck ventilation. Another key focus area is improved wall insulation, which includes developing dynamic membrane materials that offer improved thermal and moisture performance. Research aimed at reducing energy losses through basements is also being conducted as a part of envelope R&D.

HVAC and Water Heating

Space conditioning (heating and cooling) and water heating account for 45% of energy end use in the buildings sector.[4] R&D activity in this area is targeting an 80% reduction in the energy consumption of commercial HVAC and residential water heating equipment by 2020 (compared with 2004 baseline levels). BTP is continuing to support development of an integrated heat pump system that can meet multiple space conditioning needs (e.g., air heating, cooling, and dehumidifying, along with water heating). Another subset of the HVAC and water heating R&D area is solar heating and cooling, which is developing technologies that capture the sun's energy to help meet various electrical and thermal loads of energy-efficient buildings and homes.

Lighting

The goal of lighting R&D is to develop lighting technologies with significantly increased efficacies[5] compared with today's most efficient lighting products. The primary focus of this research is solid-state lighting (SSL) materials and devices, which include both light-emitting diodes (LEDs) and organic light-emitting diodes (OLEDs). In addition to efficacy, key performance metrics for new lighting technologies include high-quality color rendering (measured by a device's color rendering index and correlated color temperature) and increased product lifetime. BTP-sponsored SSL activities include core technology R&D, product development, and improved manufacturing techniques to reduce costs and enhance product quality. BTP lighting activities also support the Bright Tomorrow Lighting Prize (L Prize), a DOE-sponsored competition designed to encourage lighting manufacturers to develop high-efficiency SSL products that will replace common incandescent light bulbs.

Windows

Windows play an important role in determining a building's energy efficiency and the quality of living/ working conditions for its occupants. Dynamic windows and advanced fenestration systems are being developed that can adjust to varying conditions and improve the insulating performance of windows to a target value of R10. Such systems are also being designed to preferentially transmit visible light while reducing solar heat gain. The use of natural daylighting in buildings reduces energy consumption from artificial lighting sources and improves occupants' sense of connection to the outdoors. BTP is focused on developing advanced materials and manufacturing processes that can deliver cost-effective dynamic window systems with a high level of durability.

Many of the activities conducted in the envelope and windows areas are not aimed at producing new commercial products, but involve design guides and strategies for reducing building energy consumption (e.g., recommendations for how to best implement existing technologies). A lot of this work involves information dissemination to the public (e.g., through free software tools) and advances the science of energy-efficient building construction (e.g., closed crawl spaces and advanced attic/roof systems), but does not result in commercially available products. This report focuses on the development of specific technological advances that are sold as commercial products. For this reason, some major successes from the envelope and windows areas (e.g., the High Performance Windows Volume Purchase Program and free versions of the WUFI-ORNL/IBP, WINDOW, and THERM software programs) are not included in this document.

Investment in energy-efficiency R&D for the core areas described above offers significant potential for reducing U.S. energy consumption and greenhouse gas emissions. As shown in Figure 1.1, buildings accounted for 40% of U.S. primary energy consumption in 2008, more than any other individual sector of the U.S. economy.[4]

Space conditioning, lighting, and water heating account for 60% of energy end use in the buildings sector and are major target areas of technology R&D sponsored by BTP's Emerging Technologies subprogram. Activities in the envelope and windows areas also play a major role towards reducing HVAC and lighting energy use through improved insulation and natural daylight harvesting.

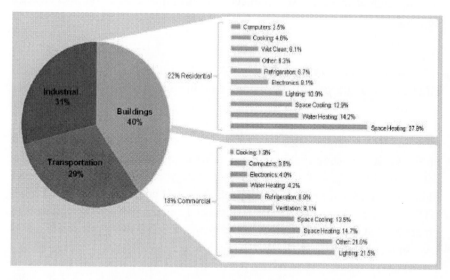

Figure 1.1. U.S. Primary Energy Consumption, 2008[4].

1.2. Contents of this Report

The remaining chapters of this report explain in greater detail the methodology used by PNNL to conduct this investigation and present the results of this effort in tables and graphics. The appendices provide details related to the data-gathering process and descriptions of each commercially available product and emerging technology identified in the study, along with a reverse directory of technology developer organizations.

2.0. APPROACH

To initiate the BTP technology tracking project, PNNL assembled a list of BTP-sponsored technology R&D projects to investigate and obtained contact information for each project's principal investigator (PI) or point of contact (POC).

This list, a "living document" that changes over time, was generated from multiple data sources that covered various sets of BTP-funded projects. Once a working version of the technology tracking list (i.e., a list including PI/POC contact information for each project) was assembled, PNNL began contacting PIs/POCs to ascertain the status of their projects. Projects resulting in commercially available products or emerging technologies qualified for additional investigation, including development of a one-page technology description and calculation of energy savings for select commercially available products. This chapter documents the process through which PNNL arrived at the initial working list of projects to investigate and provides a detailed description of the additional investigation performed for technologies identified as commercially available or emerging.

2.1. Selection of Projects to Investigate

PNNL obtained multiple lists of projects funded by BTP's Emerging Technologies subprogram and used these lists to assemble an initial pool of projects for investigation in the technology tracking effort. Projects on these lists were either kept or eliminated based on the following criteria:

- Projects ending prior to 2005 were removed from consideration based on a decision by PNNL staff and this effort's original DOE project manager. The period 2005-2009 was determined to be a good timeframe for capturing products that recently entered the market and technologies within three years of doing so.
- Projects not related to technology R&D (e.g., information centers, building energy codes and standards, and technical program management) were eliminated because they were determined to be outside the scope/focus of this effort.
- Projects terminated by DOE before their scheduled completion date or otherwise known to have failed were eliminated.

In November 2009, PNNL obtained a list of 535 projects that were from EERE's Corporate Planning System (CPS) database and that were funded by the Emerging Technologies subprogram during the past decade. The CPS data included the following information for each project: performing organization, short title, start and completion dates, and a brief project description. However, it did not include PI/POC contact information. PNNL staff narrowed down this initial list to 134 projects based on the criteria listed above.

In an effort to obtain contact information for the PIs/POCs associated with the initial list of projects, PNNL staff contacted the National Energy Technology Laboratory (NETL), which manages many BTP-funded projects. In April 2010, NETL sent PNNL three lists from their project management database that contained PI/POC contact information for different categories of projects funded by the Emerging Technologies subprogram. The first list contained 211 projects awarded to private companies and universities, the second included 86 Inter-Entity Work Orders awarded to national laboratories, and the third contained 60 congressionally-directed projects. PNNL staff worked with NETL to eliminate projects from these lists based on the criteria described above and to match up projects (and contact information) from these lists with the CPS data. The end result of this effort was an initial working list of 133 projects to investigate.

PNNL also investigated Small Business Innovation Research (SBIR) and Small Business Technology Transfer (STTR) grants awarded from 2005-2009 to organizations developing building technologies. SBIR grants are funded in two phases: Phase I grants focus on the feasibility of an idea and are funded at a low level (typically up to $100K); Phase II grants focus on R&D and are funded at a higher level (typically up to $500K). To receive a Phase II grant, a small business must have successfully completed a Phase I grant and been selected to continue their research. Like SBIR grants, STTR grants are awarded to small businesses, with the caveat that a nonprofit research institution (e.g., a university or national laboratory) must also be involved. PNNL focused on SBIR Phase II and STTR grant projects for this technology tracking effort, and 18 of these projects were added to the working list.

The final source of information used by PNNL staff to find projects for the technology tracking effort was BTP's SSL website, which contains lists of current and completed LED and OLED projects. Of the 141 projects listed on these pages, 73 qualified for inclusion on the technology tracking list. After consolidating all of these data sources into a single set and making sure that projects appearing on multiple lists were not double counted, the final working version of the technology tracking list contained 190 projects for investigation.

2.2. Technology Tracking of Commercially Available and Emerging Technologies

The PNNL team contacted the PIs/POCs for the 190 technology R&D projects to determine whether each technology was commercially available, emerging, potential,[1] or no longer being pursued. This initial round of investigation identified 11 commercially available products, 41 emerging technologies, 68 potential technologies, and 70 projects no longer being pursued. Complete lists of all the commercially available, emerging, and potential technologies are shown in Appendix A.

For technologies identified as commercially available or emerging, a template (shown in Appendix B) was sent to the PIs/ POCs to gather data on each technology. Data collected about the technologies were then entered into a BTP Technology Tracking Database. The database is divided into commercially available and emerging technology sections, each of which is sub-divided into following research categories: envelope, HVAC and water heating, lighting, and windows. BTP personnel have access to the database, which is stored at PNNL. Periodically, PNNL will transmit an updated version of the database to BTP. In addition to the electronic database, hard copy files are kept for each technology that include the template (database) information and other supporting data such as annual progress reports, presentations, and information from the technology developer's website.

Using information supplied in the templates by technology PIs/POCs, PNNL staff developed one-page descriptions for each commercially available product or emerging technology. Those one-page descriptions are shown in

Appendices C and D, respectively. PNNL staff reviewed all information received by the technology PIs/POCs for technical validity and accuracy and then gave the technology developers a chance to review the descriptions and suggest changes. An important condition of the technology tracking process is that all technology descriptions must be approved by the PIs/POCs before appearing anywhere in the public domain.

The long-term intent of the PNNL effort is to periodically contact the technology developers currently listed in this report and obtain updated status information on their projects, which will be entered into the technology tracking database.

At that time, any necessary changes will also be made to the technology descriptions (e.g., new product features or a changing R&D focus). During each cycle of technology tracking, emerging technologies that have experienced their first U.S. commercial sale will be upgraded to commercially available status, and potential technologies that have moved to within three years of commercialization will be upgraded to emerging status. At the same time, the emerging and potential technology lists will be continually replenished with newly funded BTP projects.

2.3. Quantifying Benefits of Commercially Available Technologies

One method that PNNL uses to quantify the benefits of government R&D programs is calculating the energy savings and emissions reductions realized through the use of commercially available products that made it to the marketplace with the assistance of government grant funding. Energy savings cannot be determined for some products, typically because they either do not directly take part in an energy-consuming process or have large numbers of highly variable applications and uses. For example, an improved lighting ballast and electronic driver technology can be used with many different lighting systems in a very large number of applications with varying energy consumption patterns. By comparison, residential hot water heaters are relatively homogenous in their application and energy consumption.

For a commercially available technology with quantifiable energy savings, PNNL staff work with the PI/POC to develop a calculation methodology for determining the technology's energy consumption on a per unit, per time basis. Both the PI/POC and PNNL staff must agree that the methodology is valid and accurate. PNNL staff then compare the technology's energy consumption to that of the established baseline product that the technology is intended to replace. (For example, the energy consumption of an LED lighting product can be compared with that of incandescent or fluorescent technologies providing an equivalent lumen output of light.) The difference represents the amount of energy saved from use of the technology on a per unit, per time basis. Once this methodology is finalized, the technology PI/POC must provide the number of sales/installations of their product so that the total energy savings can be computed. Many organizations treat sales information as proprietary, which often makes it impossible to quantify the energy savings for certain commercially available technologies.

Once a technology's total energy savings have been determined, impacts on the environment are calculated by estimating the associated reduction of air pollutants. This calculation is based on the type of fuel saved and the pollutants typically associated with combustion of that fuel. For example, for every million Btu of coal combusted, approximately 1.25 pounds of sulfur oxides (known acid rain precursors) are emitted to the atmosphere. Therefore, every million-Btu reduction in coal use results in the elimination of 1.25 pounds of polluting sulfur oxides.

The cumulative energy savings and emissions reductions for individual technologies are provided in the commercially available technology pages in Appendix C.

3.0. RESULTS

The results of the effort undertaken in the BTP technology tracking project are summarized in this chapter. The following pages provide a graphical analysis of the technology identification and tracking results, a brief tabular description of the technologies and their benefits, and a tabular pairing of each technology with the primary technical barrier/challenge from BTP's *Multiyear Program Plan* that it addresses.

PNNL staff identified 11 commercially available and 41 emerging technologies, which are described in detail in Appendices C and D, respectively. Figure 3.1 shows the number of commercially available and emerging technologies in each major research category. Lighting research accounts for more than half (58%) of all commercially available and emerging technologies identified, with emerging technologies comprising the vast majority (87%) of the Lighting total. The large percentage of technologies coming from the Lighting area is consistent with the fact that more than 50%

of the Emerging Technologies subprogram's total budget during 2005-2009 was allocated to Lighting R&D.

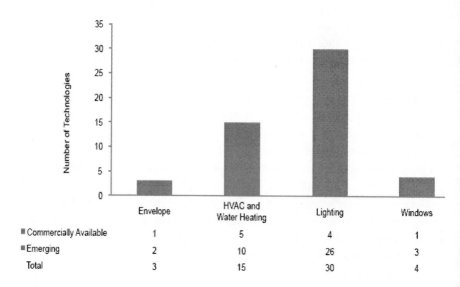

Figure 3.1. Commercially Available and Emerging Technologies by Research Category.

Another way to view the commercially available and emerging technology data, shown in Figure 3.2, is by technology developer organization type. Three types of organizations were identified: private companies, universities, and national laboratories. Private companies account for almost three quarters of all commercially available and emerging technologies, with slightly more than half of the remaining quarter being developed by national laboratories.

In addition to commercially available products and emerging technologies, PNNL identified 68 potential technologies, which are listed in Appendix A. The distribution of potential technologies by major R&D category is shown in Figure 3.3.

Lighting R&D accounts for 69% of the potential technologies, an even larger fraction than its 58% share of commercially available and emerging technologies. Potential technologies, which have the longest projected time to commercialization, typically represent the majority of projects that received their funding near the end of the analysis timeframe (in this case, 2007-2009). The majority of lighting R&D funding occurred during 2007-2009, as SSL development expanded to include the new, rapidly growing field of OLED research. This investigation identified zero commercially available OLED products, 6 emerging OLED technologies, and 22 potential OLED technologies (see Appendix A for details). This trend shows the results of increased funding levels for OLED research in the past few years. The large number of potential OLED technologies suggests that it will likely take at least 5 years before OLEDs start to make a significant penetration into the commercial marketplace.

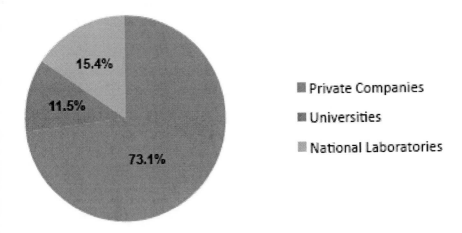

Figure 3.2. Types of Organizations with Commercially Available and Emerging Technologies.

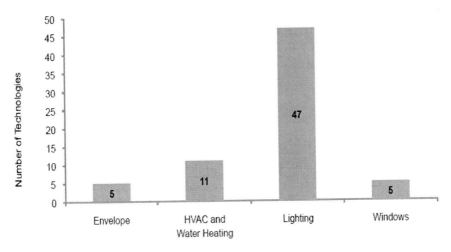

Figure 3.3. Potential Technologies by Research Category.

Because SSR is still in its infancy, BTP-funded projects in the lighting R&D area are well positioned to provide a great example of the long-term benefits of technology tracking. This effort identified only four commercially available lighting products, two of which were LED-based devices. Two-thirds of the emerging lighting technologies involve LED devices or materials, which suggests that an increased number of LED products entering the marketplace might be observed around three years from now. As mentioned above, the majority of OLED technologies fall into the potential category and are therefore likely at least five or six years away from being commercialized. In subsequent years, periodic updates to this report will allow BTP to see the results of the increased funding for SSL R&D projects that took place during 20052009. By starting the tracking process at the beginning of the SSL era, the opportunity exists to observe how many and what kind of emerging and potential lighting technologies are successfully commercialized. As trends and successful approaches to commercialization begin to emerge from analysis of this data, BTP will be able to more effectively direct future investment dollars, thereby accelerating the market penetration of energy-saving technologies.

The potential technologies can also be viewed by organization type, as shown in Figure 3.4. As with commercially available and emerging technologies, private companies represented the majority (56%) of potential technology developers. Universities more than doubled their percentage of projects from Figure 3.2 (11.5% to 25%), and national laboratories also increased their percentage (15% to 19%). The stronger representation of universities in the potential technologies distribution stems from the fact that universities often perform work with the goal of advancing fundamental scientific understanding in a particular research area and are further removed from the technology development associated with emerging and commercially available technologies.

Table 3.1 briefly describes each of the 11 commercially available technologies and their benefits. The full descriptions of these technologies are provided in Appendix C.

Table 3.2 briefly describes each of the 41 emerging technologies and their benefits. The full descriptions of these technologies are provided in Appendix D.

BTP's *Multi-Year Program Plan*, which was last updated in July 2008, was examined to see how the commercially available and emerging technologies align with the objectives and goals for technology R&D carried out by the Emerging Technologies subprogram. The plan lists technical (nonmarket) challenges/barriers for each of the four major research categories investigated in this project. The three envelope technologies in Tables 3.1 and 3.2 were found to align with three of the six technical challenges listed for that research area, as shown in Table 3.3. The 15 HVAC and water heating technologies were found to align with three of the four challenges in that area, as shown in Table 3.4. All seven lighting technical challenges were addressed by the 30 lighting technologies identified in this effort, as shown in Table 3.5. The four windows technologies were found to address two of the five challenges in that category, as shown in Table 3.6.

An alphabetized directory of the organizations that developed the commercially available and emerging technologies described in Appendices C and D is provided in Appendix E.

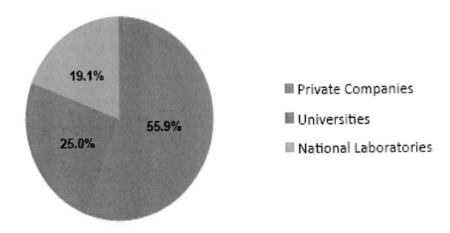

Figure 3.4. Types of Organizations with Potential Technologies.

Table 3.1. Commercially Available Technologies Summary

Technology	Organization	Description	Benefits	Commercial Status
		Envelope		
Next-Generation Envelope Materials	Oak Ridge National Laboratory	An organic, microencapsulated, fire-resistant phase change material (PCM) that improves the thermal performance of building envelopes when blended into conventional insulation materials.	Reduces heat transfer through building envelopes by absorbing heat during peak cooling hours (changing from solid to liquid) and rejecting heat to the environment (by re-solidifying) when outdoor temperatures drop.	Commercialized in 2007. Small quantities have been produced for customers wishing to test the PCM.
		HVAC and Water Heating		
Echo™: A Hybrid Solar Electric/Thermal System	PVT Solar, Inc.	A residential building solar system that provides electricity, heating, cooling, and hot water. The system can offset over 50% of a home's energy needs.	Achieves a high level of reliability by using an air-based (waterless) design. Provides a simple design that can be installed using standard roofing practices.	Commercialized in 2009. More than 50 systems installed in the U.S.
GeoSpring™ Hybrid Water Heater	General Electric Company	A commercially released hybrid water heater that uses heat pump technology to heat water. The unit uses 62% less energy than an equivalent 50 gallon electric water heater. The unit meets ENERGY STAR criteria and qualifies for federal tax credits.	Offers simple installation by using existing utility connections. A GeoSpring water heater could save the average U.S. household $300 per year on its electric bills.	Commercialized in 2009. First ENERGY STAR qualified heat pump water heater. Installed units have saved over an estimated 68 billion Btu.
NextAire™ Packaged Gas Heat Pump	IntelliChoice Energy	An 11-ton rooftop packaged heat pump for commercial buildings that uses a natural-gas-fired engine (instead of an electric motor) to drive the vapor compression refrigerant cycle.	Reduces operating costs by avoiding expensive demand and time-of-use electricity charges. Saves 0.5 gallons of water per kWh compared with similar-sized units consuming grid-generated electricity.	Commercialized in 2010, with 50 units installed in the U.S.

Technology	Organization	Description	Benefits	Commercial Status
Quiet Climate 2: Efficient Heat Pump for Portable Classrooms	Bard Manufacturing Company, Inc..	A 3- to 5-ton wall-mounted heat pump for portable classrooms. The unit improves classroom conditions by reducing HVAC-related noise and improving indoor air quality.	Reduces audible noise levels to ≤42 dB while operating and ≤35 dB while in fan-only mode for ventilation. Delivers 480 CFM of ventilation air or 15 CFM per occupant in a 32-person classroom.	Commercialized in 2008 and used in several schools throughout the U.S.
Vertex™ Residential Gas Condensing Water Heater	A.O. Smith Corporation	A product line of high efficiency gas water heaters. Lower cost and high performance were achieved by using standard heater components and strategic material choice and design strategies.	Installs easily using existing utility connections. Provides cost effective design with reliable performance. Achieves up to 30% energy savings compared with conventional gas water heaters.	Commercialized in 2006. Available nationwide.
		Lighting - LED Devices		
High-Efficiency LED Lamp for Solid-State Lighting	Cree, Inc.	An LED high-power chip with an efficacy in excess of 92 lm/W for warm white and 120 lm/W for cool white. These chips, when packaged with an appropriate phosphor and optics for maximum light extraction, will produce LEDs suitable for SSL products.	Offers compatibility with low-cost phosphor application processes and simplifies white LED manufacturing. Increases lighting efficacy by up to 10 times compared with incandescent light bulbs. Enables customization of device geometry for different applications.	Commercialized in 2006. Continuing development to increase cool and warm white high-power LED performance. Over 1 billion LED chips have been sold worldwide.
Integrated, Solid-State LED Luminaire for General Lighting	Philips Color Kinetics	LED-based A-lamp and parabolic aluminum reflector (PAR) lamp replacement products. The technology was used for the L-Prize competition entry.	Achieves 25,000 hours lifetime and an 80% gain in energy efficiency compared with industry standard A-lamp equivalents.	Commercialized in 2009. Continuing development to meet ENERGY STAR criteria.

Table 3.1. (Continued)

Technology	Organization	Description	Benefits	Commercial Status
		Lighting - Other		
Adapting Wireless Technology for Lighting Control	ELB Electronics, Inc.	A system of advanced wireless controls for lighting applications, including wireless-controllable actuators, electronic dimmable lamp ballasts, and sensors for light level and occupancy detection.	Reduces lighting energy consumption by monitoring occupancy and by integrating daylighting schemes. Achieves full-range dimming in fluorescent lamp ballasts.	Commercialized in 2007. Continuing development with Zigbee™ communication capabilities.
Ballast/Driver Technology for Metal Halide or Solid-State Lighting Systems	Energy Focus, Inc.	An electronic ballast/driver for optimizing lamp start-up and operation and for instantly switching on metal halide lamps or SSL systems.	Provides 92% efficient ballast circuitry and improves output lm/W and operational lifetime. Achieves military specifications and energy savings up to 80% compared with conventional lighting systems.	Commercialized in 2009. Developing SSL products for general and hazardous environment lightingapplications.
		Windows		
SageGlass® Electrochromic Windows	SAGE Electrochromics, Inc.	Electrochromic window glazing that preserves natural daylight benefits. Glazing fully functions as a conventional insulating window but can be tinted to reduce sun glare and solar heat gain.	Can be used for either residential or commercial applications. Blocks glare without loss of visibility or comfort. Provides proven product durability and reliability.	Commercialized in 2007. Installed units have saved an estimated two billion Btu.

Table 3.2. Emerging Technologies Summary

Technology	Organization	Description	Benefits
Envelope			
Insulating Form System for Concrete Foundation Edges	Davis Energy Group, Inc.	A leave-in-place concrete slab form board that also serves as insulation. The product consists of PVC extrusion and Styrofoam™ filler, which reduces foundation heat loss.	Reduces greenhouse gas emissions by lowering building heating loads. Prevents termite damage to wall framing and reduces construction waste.
Three-Dimensional Building Energy Performance Measurement and Modeling System	University of Nebraska-Lincoln	A system that generates a 3D model of a building's envelope with thermal resistance information for the envelope materials (e.g., walls, roofs, windows, and doors) stored at each point in space.	Offers visual information about building envelope energy performance, which is easier for homeowners to understand compared with numerical or graphical data. Helps building owners make informed envelope technology retrofit decisions.
HVAC and Water Heating			
Accurate Feed-Forward Temperature Control for Tankless Water Heaters	Building Solutions, Inc.	A new algorithm that improves temperature control in tankless water heaters by incorporating feed-forward control.	Improves the ability of tankless water heaters to maintain a specified outlet temperature and to quickly respond to changing flowrates.
Air Bearing Heat Exchanger	Sandia National Laboratories	An air bearing heat exchanger that uses an air gap as the transfer medium between a heat sink and a rotating impeller. The rotating finned design significantly improves cooling and is not susceptible to dust or dirt fouling.	Maximizes translation of mechanical work into relative motion and reduces audible noise. Improves cooling capacity by up to 10 times.
Ammonia Absorption Technologies for HVAC Systems	Rocky Research	Innovative technologies that provide energy-efficient absorption space conditioning for residential and light commercial applications.	Reduces the chances of brownouts and blackouts during summer heat waves when stress on the electrical grid from air conditioning loads is exceptionally high.

Table 3.2. (Continued)

Technology	Organization	Description	Benefits
Comboflair®: An Integrated HVAC and Water Heating System	DeLima Associates	A 2- to 4-ton packaged HVAC unit for manufactured homes. Cooling is provided via a vapor-compression system. A natural gas water heater provides space heating (via a hydronic coil) and hot water for the home.	Reduces manufactured home energy costs compared with separate water heating and electric resistance space heating arrangements. Offers easy installation and a small footprint for minimal space consumption.
Energy-Efficient Façades for Green Buildings	Rensselaer Polytechnic Institute - CASE	A building façade using solar cells to provide electricity and heating. The system can also integrate into daylight harvesting schemes, thus enhancing interior lighting quality and reducing the need for artificial lighting.	Reduces building cooling and lighting equipment requirements and operationcosts. Achieves 80% energy efficiencyin cooling, heating, and lighting.
Foundation Heat Pump	Oak Ridge National Laboratory	A ground source heat pump that takes advantage of the ground's moderate temperatures (relative to air temperatures) to increase heating/cooling efficiency compared with conventional air source heat pumps.	Reduces HVAC energy consumption and operating cost. Uses a home's existing excavated foundation and utility trenches to minimize installation cost.
HyPak: A High-Efficiency Rooftop Packaged HVAC System	Davis Energy Group, Inc.	A 10 to 30-ton rooftop HVAC system that provides energy-efficient space conditioning in commercial buildings.	Reduces peak HVAC electricity consumption by using evaporative cooling, which is most effective at high outdoor temperatures.
Improving Electric Motor Efficiency	SMMA – The Motor & Motion Association	An electric motor test method, test and measurement system and a software simulation and design package to improve motor efficiency. The expanded capability of the simulation and design package has demonstrated excellent agreement between simulation and actual prototype test and measurement.	Automates testing procedures and streamlines the motor design and development process. Improves electric motor performance and efficiency.

Technology	Organization	Description	Benefits
Predictive Optimal Control of Active and Passive Building Thermal Storage Inventory	Clean Urban Energy, Inc.	A control technology that predictively optimizes thermal storage strategies in commercial buildings to shift HVAC electricity consumption from peak to non-peak hours.	Reduces HVAC operating costs. Increases grid efficiency by shifting consumption from peaking power plants to more efficient baseload plants. Reduces daytime strain on thegrid and helps combat the problem of negative nighttime electricity prices due to an excess of generation capacity and a lack of demand.
Thermoelectric Materials for Waste Heat Recovery	Hi-Z Technology, Inc.	A thermoelectric (TE) material with an efficiency three times that of typical TEs. A TE with increased efficiency could be used to recover waste heat and as an alternative method for conventional refrigeration and air-conditioning systems.	Reduces manufacturing costs using an automated process and readily available Si, C, B, and N. Avoids using toxic and expensive materials.
Lighting - LED Devices			
100 Lumen/Watt Warm White LED	Philips Lumileds Lighting Company	An LED using a new phosphor technology to achieve a warm-white color temperature and color rendering index of 90. Work continues to develop larger, high-power LED packages.	Reduces cost per lumen and energy consumption of general lighting applications. Offers an expected LED product lifetime in excess of 50,000 hours.
Affordable, High-Efficiency Solid-State Downlight Luminaires with Novel Cooling	GE Global Research	Synthetic jet cooling to increase heat sink thermal transfer rates, allowing LEDs to be driven at higher currents. The increased lumen output per LED reduces the number of LEDs required by up to 40%.	Reduces system cost by using improved thermal management, which results in increased lumens per LED and reduced LED chip count. Offers a compact design that is half the size and weight of a 600 lumen, passively cooled lamp.

Table 3.2. (Continued)

Technology	Organization	Description	Benefits
Efficient LED System-in-Module for General Lighting	Philips Lighting	An Edison-based SSL device for general illumination. The device offers an operational lifetime of 50,000 hrs and has integrated control circuitry for color variability and light level control. The device is computer controllable via wire or wireless communications.	Offers adjustable color and light output that can be programmed for differing applications. Provides compatible device programming with daylight harvesting schemes and usage (occupancy).
LECD Technology for Lighting and Signage	Ecer Technologies, LLC	Electro-ceramescent technology for a variety of lighting and signage applications. These devices use layers of ceramic and phosphor materials deposited on a thin sheet of steel. The devices are durable and require very little power to operate.	Offers product lifetime of >50,000 hours. Avoids heat production or de-lamination over time. Requires one-tenth of the energy consumed by similar LED applications. Provides nonglaring light in response to the dark-sky initiative.
Scaling Up: Kilo-Lumen SSL Exceeding 100 Lumens per Watt	Light Prescriptions Innovators, LLC	An efficient LED-based light bulb replacement that produces 90 lm/W. The device uses a remote phosphor approach that achieves excellent color rendering. The device is dimmable and internally adjusts output to prevent damage from overheating.	Achieves 25,000 hours operating lifetime. Provides good quality light and can be used as an energy-efficient alternative to conventional incandescent, compact fluorescent, or fluorescent lighting.
Lighting - LED Materials			
Bulk GaN Substrate Growth Technique	Sandia National Laboratories	A cost effective approach using electrochemical solution growth to produce bulk GaN substrates. The process is scalable and produces high quality bulk GaN materials compatible with current wafer substrate manufacturing processes.	Uses proven concepts from existing crystal growth applications. Produces GaN boules of industry-desired diameters for wafer substrates. Produces many different types of solid-state devices across multiple markets.

Technology	Organization	Description	Benefits
Enhancing Quantum Efficiency of InGaN-Based LEDs	Lehigh University - Packard Laboratory	Lattice structure improvements such as staggered InGaN quantum wells to increase the internal quantum efficiency of nitride LEDs.	Increases the output power, efficiency, and lifetime of InGaN-based LEDs.
Growth Technique for Large-Diameter AlN Single Crystal	Fairfield Crystal Technology, LLC	AlN substrate growth process for the fabrication of highly efficient LEDs. The process produces substrates that result in device expitaxy with fewer defects, which reduce LED device performance and durability.	Produces substrates with fewer defects, which improves device yield. Improves product lifetime and device performance.
High-Efficiency, Nanocomposite White Light Phosphors	Nanosys, Inc.	Remote phosphors based on quantum dot technology to improve the efficiency and color of SSL products. Remote phosphors can be tuned to specific wavelengths and incorporated into existing manufacturing processes.	Provides color stability and improved lifetime, efficiency, and color rendering. Can be easily modified to produce products for different applications.
High-Efficiency Nitride-Based Solid-State Lighting	University of California, Santa Barbara	Use of bulk, non-polar GaN substrates in the fabrication process. The neutral polarity of the substrates reduces "LED efficiency droop" at high current density.	Provides an expected LED life of 50,000 hours. Improves internal and external light extraction efficiencies.
High-Efficiency, Non-Polar, GaN-Based LEDs	Inlustra Technologies, Inc.	GaN devices using native GaN substrates to manipulate the crystalline structure and minimize the number of defects. This approach promotes higher electrical-tooptical efficiency at increased drive current to produce more light per LED.	Reduces cost by using shorter layer deposition times and simplified fabrication schemes. Improves LED efficacy, durability and lifetime.
High-Performance Green LEDs	Rensselaer Polytechnic Institute	A high-efficiency green AlGaInN LED using high-quality bulk GaN. The epitaxial process controls material properties like piezoelectric polarization to improve device quality and performance, especially at high injection currents.	Reduces cost by using large-scale bulk GaN substrates. Eliminates phosphor aging and maintains color stability. Increases efficiency by eliminating conventional LED phosphor-excitation losses.

Table 3.2. (Continued)

Technology	Organization	Description	Benefits
High-Performance Structured OLEDs and LEDs	Lawrence Berkeley National Laboratory	A technique using micro- and nanostructured processes for improved OLED light extraction efficiency and high-quality crystalline structures for OLEDs and LEDs. The processes use materials that are less reactive, insensitive to air or water, and much easier to use in manufacturing.	Improves product lifetime and performance. Simplifies manufacturing by using imprint-based fabrication and vapor deposition steps.
Key Technologies for White Lighting Based on LEDs: Precise Temperature Measurement	Sandia National Laboratories	An ultraviolet pyrometer to measure process temperature and provide epitaxy temperature control that was previously not possible.	Reduces the LED fabrication costs by improving production control and yield. Allows specific InGaN device parameters (e.g., emission wavelength) to be targeted.
Nanowire-Templated Lateral Epitaxy of Low-Dislocation-Density GaN	Sandia National Laboratories	An innovative and inexpensive GaN crystal growth technique for fabricating LEDs. The process uses GaN nanowires to grow high-quality, low-defect GaN films on sapphire substrates. Lower defects in GaN improve LED device durability, reliability, and efficiency, which are needed for widespread adoption of SSL.	Provides a single-step process with reduced cost and complexity compared with other defect reduction methods. Low-defect density improves device quality, leading to increased device output and lifetime.
Phosphor-Free Solid-State Lighting Sources	Cermet Inc.	A phosphor-free approach using blue LEDs and red, green and blue dopants for producing white light. This approach improves durability, efficacy, and color temperature.	Reduces fabrication cost of white LEDs by combining multiple processesinto one step. Uses typical substrate growth techniques for LED epitaxy.

Technology	Organization	Description	Benefits
Photoluminescent Nanofibers for High-Efficiency Solid-State Lighting Phosphors	Research Triangle Institute	Polymer nanofibers for use in optical diffusers and photoluminescent materials to improve LED light output. The materials can be adjusted to provide the desired light output with high color rendering and an efficacy in excess of 55 lm/W.	Provides a cost-effective solution for diffuse, high-reflectance light management across the visible spectrum. Can be used in various geometries imposed by light fixtures, thus enabling new approaches to lighting designs.
Lighting - OLEDs			
Efficient Large-Area WOLED Lighting	Universal Display Corporation	White organic LEDs (WOLEDs) for large-area illumination. WOLEDs are energy-efficient, diffuse light sources. WOLED panels are also transparent in the off state, allowing integration into daylight harvesting schemes.	Reduces operating costs relative to conventional lighting. Can be fabricated on flexible substrates, including glass, plastics, and thin stainless steel.
Highly Efficient OLEDs For General Illumination	Physical Optics Corporation	A technology for increasing OLED energy efficiency by improving light extraction from device structure. The technique deposits a light scattering layer inside the OLED, thereby increasing photon extraction efficiency, light output uniformity, and color rendering.	Improves energy efficiency, light output uniformity, and color rendering. Provides compatibility with established OLED manufacturing techniques, including high-volume processing. Can be applied to rigid or flexible substrates.
Low-Cost, High-Efficiency Polymer OLEDs Based on Stable p-i-n Device Architecture	Add-Vision, Inc.	An OLED manufacturing process that uses roll-based printing of phosphorescent emitters on doped polymer materials. The OLEDs are flexible and can be manufactured in various widths without the need for a controlled clean-room environment.	Reduces manufacturing costs. Maximizes device efficiency by using solution-based phosphorescent materials and p-i-n doping architectures.
OLEDs for General Lighting	GE Global Research	Energy-efficient OLEDs that can be manufactured on flexible substrates using low-cost printing techniques. Flexible OLEDs could be used for portable roll-displays or displays with curved surfaces.	Offers low-cost manufacturing using high-volume, roll-to-roll manufacturing. Can be used in applications that wouldnot be feasible with traditional light sources. Provides compatibility with a variety substrates such as plastic, glass, and thin metal foil.

Table 3.2. (Continued)

Technology	Organization	Description	Benefits
Transparent Conducting Oxides and Undercoat Technologies for Economical OLED Lighting	Arkema Inc.	A zinc-based transparent conductive material and an atmospheric pressure chemical vapor deposition process for processing OLED glass substrates. The substrates can be used an alternative to indium-tin-oxide (ITO) coated glass substrates.	Achieves >90% transmission in the visible spectrum. Offers material and performance specifications equivalent to commercially available ITO.
Transparent Conductive Oxides for OLEDs	Pacific Northwest National Laboratory	A low-temperature RF magnetron sputtering process to deposit indium-free, gallium-zinc-oxide (GZO) thin films to replace costly indium-tin-oxide. GZO is suitable for glass or flexible substrates, and the deposition process is scalable to large-area high-volume manufacturing.	Reduces costs by replacing indium with more abundant materials. Reduces energy consumed for lighting applications by increasing OLED efficiency. Enables high-volume manufacturing on flexible substrates.
Lighting - Other			
Advanced Coatings to Improve the Efficiency, Color Rendering, and Life of High-Intensity-Discharge Lamps	Acree Technologies Inc.	An inexpensive, robust, single-layer coating for increasing efficacy. The coating increases the plasma temperature, thus increasing lumen output and color rendering index. The coating is applied in a single step and is compatible with large-scale production.	Improves lamp efficacy, significantly reducing lighting cost and energy consumption. Provides a robust coating that lasts throughout the lifetime of the HID lamp. Improves light output and color rendering index of the lamp.
Optical Fiber Polymer Processing Techniques for Distributed Lighting	Energy Focus, Inc.	Inexpensive large core plastic optical fibers for producing energy-efficient and cost-effective accent lighting alternatives. The plastic fibers reduce the lamp count in distributed lighting systems and lower installation and maintenance costs.	Increases energy efficiency and reduces cost of ownership of distributed accent lighting systems. Achieves simple installation requiring fewer lamps and electrical connections.

Technology	Organization	Description	Benefits
Selective, Emitter-Based, Energy-Efficient Incandescent Lamp Technology	Surmet Corporation	Two approaches to place refractory coatings on tungsten lamp filaments. The coatings are durable and have low emissivity in the infrared region. The coating process does not impact the existing lamp production process.	Improves incandescent lamp efficacy without incurring the cost premium associated with more efficient lighting products (e.g., halogen or compact fluorescent lamps). Integrates easily into existing high-volume incandescent lamp production lines.
Windows			
Adaptive Liquid Crystal Windows	AlphaMicron, Inc.	An active window glazing technology using liquid crystal deposited on flexible substrates. The process is compatible with high-volume roll-to-roll manufacturing.	Manipulates daylight transmission without excessive glare or darkness. Reduces emissions by lowering building energy consumption. Adapts to residential and commercial applications.
Advanced Framing System with Low-Emissivity Paint for Commercial Windows	Three Rivers Aluminum Company	Window framing technology that uses low-emissivity coatings and advanced thermal break and foam-filling techniques for improved U-value. The techniques have improved U-values by as much as 30% and IR emissivity by 25%.	Reduces HVAC costs by inhibiting heat transfer through aluminum window frames. Allows low-emissivity coating to be applied to existing framing systems without any additional modifications.
Vacuum Glazing Development	EverSealed Windows, Inc.	A window frame sealing technology that provides a longer-lasting vacuum insulated glass window. The technique uses a gas-tight flexible metal seal that accommodates thermal expansion and contraction with a proprietary glass-to-metal bonding material.	Increases window lifetime by using a flexible, hermetically bonded seal. Reduces energy loss through windows. Provides compatibility with various glass types as required by city or county building codes.

Table 3.3. Envelope Technical Challenges/Barriers and Related Technologies

Technical Challenges/Barriers*	Technology Title	Organization
Thermal performance versus durability performance	Insulating Form System for Concrete Foundation Edges	Davis Energy Group, Inc.
Unknown interactions	Three-Dimensional Building Energy Performance Measurement and Modeling System	University of Nebraska-Lincoln
Material developments	Next-Generation Envelope Materials	Oak Ridge National Laboratory

Table 3.4. HVAC and Water Heating Technical Challenges/Barriers

Technical Challenges/Barriers*	Technology Title	Organization
Achieving high efficiency in low-capacity HVAC systems	Ammonia Absorption Technologies for HVAC Systems	Rocky Research
	Comboflair®: An Integrated HVAC and Water Heating System	DeLima Associates
	Echo™: A Hybrid Solar Electric/Thermal System	PVT Solar, Inc.
	Energy-Efficient Facades for Green Buildings	Rensselaer Polytechnic Institute - CASE
System efficiency	Accurate Feed-Forward Temperature Control for Tankless Water Heaters	Building Solutions, Inc.
	Air Bearing Heat Exchanger	Sandia National Laboratories
	Foundation Heat Pump	Oak Ridge National Laboratory
	GeoSpring™ Hybrid Water Heater	General Electric Company
	HyPak: A High-Efficiency Rooftop Packaged HVAC System	Davis Energy Group, Inc.
	Improving Electric Motor Efficiency	SMMA - The Motor & Motion Association
	NextAire™ Packaged Gas Heat Pump	IntelliChoice Energy
	Predictive Optimal Control of Active and Passive Building Thermal Storage Inventory	Clean Urban Energy, Inc.

Technical Challenges/Barriers*	Technology Title	Organization
	Thermoelectric Materials for Waste Heat Recovery	Hi-Z Technology, Inc.
	Vertex™ Residential Gas Condensing Water Heater	A.O. Smith Corporation
Ensuring comfort and indoor environmental quality	Quiet Climate 2: Efficient Heat Pump for Portable Classrooms	Bard Manufacturing Company, Inc.

* Note: The challenges/barriers are described in the 2008 BTP Multi-Year Program Plan at
http://www1.eere.energy.gov/buildings/publications/pdfs/corporate/myp08research_ch2.pdf.

Table 3.5. Lighting Technical Barriers and Related Technologies

Technical Challenges/Barriers*	Technology Title	Organization
Luminous efficacy	100 Lumen/Watt Warm White LED	Philips Lumileds Lighting Company
	Advanced Coatings to Improve the Efficiency, Color Rendering, and Life of High-Intensity-Discharge Lamps	Acree Technologies Inc.
	High-Efficiency, Nanocomposite White Light Phosphors	Nanosys, Inc.
	High-Efficiency Nitride-Based Solid-State Lighting	University of California, Santa Barbara
	High-Performance Green LEDs	Rensselaer Polytechnic Institute
	Highly Efficient OLEDs For General Illumination	Physical Optics Corporation
	Integrated, Solid-State LED Luminaire for General Lighting	Philips Color Kinetics
	Phosphor-Free Solid-State Lighting Sources	Cermet Inc.
	Photoluminescent Nanofibers for High-Efficiency Solid-State Lighting Phosphors	Research Triangle Institute
	Scaling Up: Kilo-Lumen SSL Exceeding 100 Lumens per Watt	Light Prescriptions Innovators, LLC
	Selective, Emitter-Based, Energy-Efficient Incandescent Lamp Technology	Surmet Corporation

Table 3.5. (Continued)

Technical Challenges/Barriers*	Technology Title	Organization
Quantum efficiency	Bulk GaN Substrate Growth Technique	Sandia National Laboratories
	Enhancing Quantum Efficiency of InGaN-Based LEDs	Lehigh University - Packard Laboratory
	Growth Technique for Large-Diameter AlN Single Crystal	Fairfield Crystal Technology, LLC
	High-Efficiency, Non-Polar, GaN-Based LEDs	Inlustra Technologies, Inc.
	High-Performance Structured OLEDs and LEDs	Lawrence Berkeley National Laboratory
	Nanowire-Templated Lateral Epitaxy of Low-Dislocation-Density GaN	Sandia National Laboratories
Lifetime	Affordable, High-Efficiency Solid-State Downlight Luminaires with Novel Cooling	GE Global Research
	LECD Technology for Lighting and Signage	Ecer Technologies, LLC
Stability	Efficient LED System-in-Module for General Lighting	Philips Lighting
Packaging and manufacturing	Efficient Large-Area WOLED Lighting	Universal Display Corporation
	High-Efficiency LED Lamp for Solid-State Lighting	Cree, Inc.
	Low-Cost, High-Efficiency Polymer OLEDs Based on Stable p-i-n Device Architecture	Add-Vision, Inc.
	OLEDs for General Lighting	GE Global Research
	Transparent Conducting Oxides and Undercoat Technologies for Economical OLED Lighting	Arkema Inc.
Infrastructure	Adapting Wireless Technology for Lighting Control	ELB Electronics, Inc.
	Ballast/Driver Technology for Metal Halide or Solid-State Lighting Systems	Energy Focus, Inc.
	Optical Fiber Polymer Processing Techniques for Distributed Lighting	Energy Focus, Inc.
Cost reduction	Key Technologies for White Lighting Based on LEDs: Precise Temperature Measurement	Sandia National Laboratories
	Transparent Conductive Oxides for OLEDs	Pacific Northwest National Laboratory

* Note: The challenges/barriers are described in the 2008 BTP *Multi-Year Program Plan* at
http://www1.eere.energy.gov/buildings/publications/pdfs/corporate/myp08research_ch2.pdf.

Table 3.6. Windows Technical Challenges/Barriers and Related Technologies

Technical Challenges/Barriers*		Organization
Inability to predict performance	Adaptive Liquid Crystal Windows	AlphaMicron, Inc.
	SageGlass® Electrochromic Windows	SAGE Electrochromics, Inc.
Durability issues	Advanced Framing System with Low-Emissivity Paint for Commercial Windows	Three Rivers Aluminum Company
	Vacuum Glazing Development	EverSealed Windows, Inc.

* Note: The challenges/barriers are described in the 2008 BTP *Multi-Year Program Plan* at
http://www1.eere.energy.gov/buildings/publications/pdfs/corporate/myp08research_ch2.pdf.

APPENDIX A: TECHNOLOGY TRACKING LISTS

Commercially Available Technologies

Technology Title			Organization
Envelope		Next-Generation Envelope Materials	Oak Ridge National Laboratory
HVAC and Water Heating		Echo™: A Hybrid Solar Electric/Thermal System	PVT Solar, Inc.
		GeoSpring™ Hybrid Water Heater	General Electric Company
		NextAire™ Packaged Gas Heat Pump	IntelliChoice Energy
		Quiet Climate 2: Efficient Heat Pump for Portable Classrooms	Bard Manufacturing Company, Inc.
		Vertex™ Residential Gas Condensing Water Heater	A.O Smith Corporation
Lighting	LED Devices	High-Efficiency LED Lamp for Solid-State Lighting	Cree, Inc.
		Integrated, Solid-State LED Luminaire for General Lighting	Philips Color Kinetics
	LED Materials	N/A	N/A
	OLEDs	N/A	N/A
	Other	Adapting Wireless Technology for Lighting Control	ELB Electronics, Inc.
		Ballast/Driver Technology for Metal Halide or Solid-State Lighting Systems	Energy Focus, Inc.
Windows		SageGlass®Electrochromic Windows	SAGE Electrochromics, Inc.

Emerging Technologies

Technology Title			Organization
Envelope		Insulating Form System for Concrete Foundation Edges	Davis Energy Group, Inc.
		Three-Dimensional Building Energy Performance Measurement and Modeling System	University of Nebraska-Lincoln
HVAC and Water Heating		Accurate Feed-Forward Temperature Control for Tankless Water Heaters	Building Solutions, Inc.
		Air Bearing Heat Exchanger	Sandia National Laboratories
		Ammonia Absorption Technologies for HVAC Systems	Rocky Research
		Comboflair®: An Integrated HVAC and Water Heating System	DeLima Associates
		Energy-Efficient Facades for Green Buildings	Rensselaer Polytechnic Institute - CASE
		Foundation Heat Pump	Oak Ridge National Laboratory
		HyPak: A High-Efficiency Rooftop Packaged HVAC System	Davis Energy Group, Inc.
		Improving Electric Motor Efficiency	SMMA - The Motor & Motion Association
		Predictive Optimal Control of Active and Passive Building Thermal Storage Inventory	Clean Urban Energy, Inc.
		Thermoelectric Materials for Waste Heat Recovery	Hi-Z Technology, Inc.
Lighting	LED Devices	100 Lumen/Watt Warm White LED	Philips Lumileds Lighting Company
		Affordable, High-Efficiency Solid-State Downlight Luminaires with Novel Cooling	GE Global Research
		Efficient LED System-in-Module for General Lighting	Philips Lighting
		LECD Technology for Lighting and Signage	Ecer Technologies, LLC
		Scaling Up: Kilo-Lumen SSL Exceeding 100 Lumens per Watt	Light Prescriptions Innovators, LLC
	LED Materials	Bulk GaN Substrate Growth Technique	Sandia National Laboratories
		Enhancing Quantum Efficiency of InGaN-Based LEDs	Lehigh University - Packard Laboratory
		Growth Technique for Large-Diameter AlN Single Crystal	Fairfield Crystal Technology, LLC
		High-Efficiency, Nanocomposite White Light Phosphors	Nanosys, Inc.
		High-Efficiency Nitride-Based Solid-State Lighting	University of California, Santa Barbara
		High-Efficiency, Non-Polar, GaN-Based LEDs	Inlustra Technologies, Inc.
		High-Performance Green LEDs	Rensselaer Polytechnic Institute

Technology Title		Organization
	High-Performance Structured OLEDs and LEDs	Lawrence Berkeley National Laboratory
	Key Technologies for White Lighting Based on LEDs: Precise Temperature Measurement	Sandia National Laboratories
	Nanowire-Templated Lateral Epitaxy of Low-Dislocation-Density GaN	Sandia National Laboratories
	Phosphor-Free Solid-State Lighting Sources	Cermet Inc.
	Photoluminescent Nanofibers for High-Efficiency Solid-State Lighting Phosphors	Research Triangle Institute
OLEDs	Efficient Large Area WOLED Lighting	Universal Display Corporation
	Highly Efficient OLEDs For General Illumination	Physical Optics Corporation
	Low-Cost, High-Efficiency Polymer OLEDs Based on Stable p-i-n Device Architecture	Add-Vision, Inc.
	OLEDs for General Lighting	GE Global Research
	Transparent Conducting Oxides and Undercoat Technologies for Economical OLED Lighting	Arkema Inc.
	Transparent Coductive Oxides for OLEDs	Pacific Northwest National Laboratory
Other	Advanced Coatings to Improve the Efficiency, Color Rendering, and Life of High-Intensity-Discharge Lamps	Acree Technologies Inc.
	Optical Fiber Polymer Processing Techniques for Distributed Lighting	Energy Focus, Inc.
	Selective, Emitter-Based, Energy-Efficient Incandescent Lamp Technology	Surmet Corporation
	Adaptive Liquid Crystal Windows	AlphaMicron, Inc.
Windows	Advanced Framing System with Low-Emissivity Paint for Commercial Windows	Three Rivers Aluminum Company
	Vacuum Glazing Development	EverSealed Windows, Inc..

Potential Technologies

Technology Title		Organization
Envelope	Advanced Building Envelope Surface Materials	Lawrence Berkeley National Laboratory
	Advanced Energy Efficient Roof Systems	University of Minnesota
	Advanced Engineered Manufacturing Methods & Materials for Environmentally Benign and Energy Efficient Housing	Institute for Advanced Learning and Research
	Advanced Wall Systems	Oak Ridge National Laboratory
	Air Barriers	Oak Ridge National Laboratory
	Adaptive Full-Spectrum Solar Energy Systems	University of Nevada, Reno
	Advanced Efficient Building Testbed Initiative	Carnegie Mellon University
	Clean Technology Commercialization Initiative (PA)	Ben Franklin Technology Partners
	Converging Redundant Sensor Network Information for Improved Building Control	University of Nebraska - Lincoln
HVAC and Water Heating	Heat Pump R&D	Oak Ridge National Laboratory
	High Technology Centrifugal Compressor for Commercial Air Conditioning Systems	State of Connecticut
	Magnetic Refrigeration Technology	Astronautics Corporation of America
	Solar Electric/Thermal Pathways to ZEH-National Renewable Energy Laboratory	National Renewable Energy Laboratory
	Solar Heating and Cooling for ZEH-Sandia	Sandia National Laboratories
	Systems Approach to an Energy Efficient Laundry Process	GE Global Research
	Wireless Infrastructure for Performance Monitoring, Diagnostics, and Control in Small Commercial Buildings	NorthWrite, Inc.
Lighting	LED Devices	Efficient White SSL Component for General Illumination	Cree, Inc.
		High Efficiency Driving Electronics for General Illumination LED Luminaires	Philips Lighting
		High Quality Down Lighting Luminaire with 73% Overall System Efficiency	Osram Sylvania Products Inc.
		Highly Efficient Small Form-Factor LED Retrofit Lamp	Osram Sylvania Products Inc.
		Light Emitting Diode Display Engineering	University of Nevada, Las Vegas

Technology	Title	Organization
		Cree, Inc.
LED Materials	SSL Luminaire with Novel Driver Architecture	
	Advanced Phosphor Technology For Efficient Lighting & Energy Harvesting	PhosphorTech Corporation
	Blue/UV LEDs with Very High Photon Conversion and Extraction Efficiency for White Lighting	Boston University
	Charge Balance in Blue Electrophosphorescent Devices	Pacific Northwest National Laboratory
	Epitaxial Growth of GaN Based LED Structures on Sacrificial Substrates	Georgia Tech Research Corporation
	Fundamental Studies of Higher Efficiency III-N LEDs for High-Efficiency High-Power Solid-State Lighting	Georgia Institute of Technology
	GaN-Ready Aluminum Nitride Substrates for Cost-Effective, Very Low Dislocation Density III-Nitride LEDs	Crystal IS, Inc.
	High Efficiency Colloidal Quantum Dot Phosphors	Eastman Kodak Company
	High Efficiency m-Plane LEDs on Low Defect Density Bulk GaN Substrates	Kaai, Inc.
	High Extraction Luminescent Materials for Solid State Lighting	PhosphorTech Corporation
	Low-Cost Substrates for High-Performance Nanorod Array LEDs	Purdue University
	Multicolor, High Efficiency, Nanotextured LEDs	Yale University
	Nanostructured High Performance Ultraviolet and Blue LEDs	Brown University
	Novel Defect Spectroscopy of InGaN Materials for Improved Green LEDs	Sandia National Laboratories
	Novel Low-Cost Technology for Solid-State Lighting	Technologies and Devices International, Inc.
	Phosphor Systems for Illumination Quality Solid State Lighting Products	GE Global Research
	Phosphors for Near UV-Emitting LEDs for Efficacious Generation of White Light	University of California, San Diego
	Ultra High P-Doping Material Research for GaN-Based Light Emitters	Technologies and Devices International, Inc.
	White LEDs Using Nanophosphor-InP Blends	Sandia National Laboratories
	White-Light Emitting Active Layers in Nitride Based Heterostructures for Phosphorless SSL	University of California, San Diego
Lighting OLEDs	Enhanced WOLEDs Outcoupling Using Low Index Grids	Universal Display Corporation
	High Efficacy Integrated Under-Cabinet Phosphorescent OLED Lighting Systems	Universal Display Corporation

(Continued)

Technology Title	Organization
High Efficacy Phosphorescent SOLED Lighting	Universal Display Corporation
High Efficiency Microcavity OLED Devices With Down-Conversion Phosphors	University of Florida
High Efficiency White TOLED Devices for Lighting Applications	Universal Display Corporation
High Efficiency, Illumination Quality White OLEDs for Lighting	GE Global Research
High Quantum Efficiency OLED Lighting Systems	GE Global Research
High Stability Organic Molecular Dopants for Maximum Power Efficiency OLEDs	Pacific Northwest National Laboratory
Long-Term OLED Device Stability via Transmission Electron Microscopy Imaging of Cross-Sectioned OLED Devices	Lawrence Berkeley National Laboratory
Low-Cost Nano-Engineered Transparent Electrodes for Highly Efficient OLED Lighting	Oak Ridge National Laboratory
Low-Voltage, High-Efficiency White Phosphorescent OLEDs	Universal Display Corporation
Multi-Faceted Scientific Strategies Towards Better Solid-State Lighting of Phosphorescent OLEDs Phosphors	University of North Texas
New Stable Cathode Materials for OLEDs	International Technology Exchange
Novel High-Performance OLED Sources	Universal Display Corporation
Novel Light Extraction Enhancements for White Phosphorescent OLEDs	Universal Display Corporation
Novel Low-Cost Organic Vapor Jet Printing of Striped High Efficiency Phosphorescent OLEDs for White Lighting	Universal Display Corporation
Novel Materials for High Efficiency White Phosphorescent OLEDs	University of Southern California
Quantum Dot Light Enhancement Substrate for OLED Solid-State Lighting	QD Vision, Inc.
Solution-Processed Small-Molecule OLED Luminaire for Interior Illumination	DuPont Displays, Inc.
Surface Plasmon Enhanced Phosphorescent Organic Light Emitting Diodes	University of California, Santa Barbara
Top-Emitting White OLEDs with Ultrahigh Light Extraction Efficiency	University of Florida
Transparent Conductive Oxide for OLEDs	National Renewable Energy Laboratory

Technology Title		Organization
	Other	
	N/A	N/A
Windows	Affordable Window Insulation With R-10/inch Rating	Aspen Aerogels, Inc.
	Electrochromic Coating Technology	Soladigm, Inc.
	Energy Efficient Triple IG Automation EEE (Triple-E)	GED Integrated Solutions
	Highly Insulating Windows With a U-Value Less Than 0.6	Aspen Aerogels, Inc.
	Solar Energy Windows and Smart IR Switchable Building Technologies	PPG Industries Inc.

APPENDIX B: TECHNOLOGY TRACKING DATA COLLECTION TEMPLATE

Commercially Available or Emerging Technology Title

Short Phrase Describing the Technology's Primary Benefits and/or Achievements	Primary Industry:
Technology History: • Who is developing the technology, and any key project partners. • If applicable, who is selling the technology and the year it became commercially available. • Current focus/direction of technology development. Applications: One or two sentences about where the technology will be used an what the impact of its use will be. Capabilities: Short phrases describing the technology's performance, preferably in a quantitative manner. • Produces… • Achieves… • Saves…	Graphic: Photo of the technology or graphic showing the process performed by the technology.
Description: This section tells the story of how the technology fills a need, and typically contains three paragraphs of about 100 words each. The first paragraph describes the situation before the technology. The second paragraph describes how the technology works and how it solves or improves upon the prior situation. The third paragraph is typically used for additional description of the technology and its advantages, and usually ends with a mention of the project's future direction. For example: "advanced prototypes have been developed and a demonstration unit will be evaluated."	Benefits: Two or three headings describing additional benefits of the technology, with a short phrase under each. Can be quantitative or qualitative in nature. Examples: Cost Savings Reduces costs by taking advantage of… Durability Improves product lifetime… Efficiency Optimizes the process by… Emissions Reductions Reduces emissions of… Safety Increases safety by detecting…

Short Phrase Describing the Technology's Primary Benefits and/or Achievements	Primary Industry:
	Productivity Enables high-volume production…
Tracking Information (PNNL Internal):	
Year Developed:	Year Commercialized:
Year First Tracked:	Year Stopped Tracking:
Associated Parties:	
DOE Manager(s) Contact information for DOE Program Manager(s). (PNNL Internal)	Technology Partner(s) Contact information for the technology PI/POC, and any project partners. For commercially available products, contact info for a sales representative is also helpful.
	Name of PI/POC
	Organization Name
	Address
	Phone
	Fax
	E-mail
	Website

Status Information (PNNL Internal)

Year:	Status:	Comments:
2010	Commercially Available or Emerging	This is a short summary of development progress in the prior calendar year, currentstatus, and future commercialization plans.

Installations & Savings (PNNL Internal)

ID	Installation	Installed	Decommissioned	Savings
	Info regarding the number of operational installations of commercially available products with energy savings.			

Description

Also Known As:
This is an alternative name for the technology if one exists.

Technical Description

This is an advanced technical description of the process/technology, typically containing information that is too detailed or discipline-specific to appear in the report's technology pages (Appendices C and D).

References

Source List:
This is a listing of any additional places where information about the technology/product can be obtained, including organization websites, DOE fact sheets, conference presentations, quarterly or annual reports, etc...

Energy Savings Calculation Methodology (PNNL Internal)

For a commercially available product with quantifiable energy savings, PNNL staff work with the technology PI/POC to calculate the approximate amount of energy saved from use of the product on a per unit, per time basis. Information specific to the technology (e.g., energy consumption, fuel type, and number of units sold) is provided by the PI/POC. PNNL staff take this information and compare the technology to the currently established product(s) that it is intended to replace, and determine the per unit, per time energy savings rate.

Remarks

History:
This is a short summary of when testing began and any major changes that have occurred over time.

General Comments

This is a section for any additional comments that a technology PI/POC would like to make that do not fit into any other section of the template.

Markets and Economics

Comments:
A short description of the markets an organization intends to reach with their technology, and any applicable information such as product lifetime, rebates, tax incentives, payback period, etc…

Selling Price

For commercially available products, technology PIs/POCs can provide the approximate sale price if their organization considers it to be publicly available information.

APPENDIX C: COMMERCIALLY AVAILABLE TECHNOLOGY DESCRIPTIONS

Next-Generation Envelope Materials

Phase Change Material Enhances Insulation Performance
Buildings consume more energy than either the transportation or industrial sectors of the U.S. economy. Energy conservation research has investigated how insulation materials can be used to provide potential savings. The performance of insulation materials can be improved by the addition of active thermal components such as phase change materials (PCMs). PCMs are solid at room temperature, melt when the temperature rises, and re-solidify as the temperature drops. When the material melts, it absorbs and stores heat, retarding heat flow into the building. When the material solidifies, it releases the stored thermal energy. Historically, PCMs have been proven to enhance building energy performance, but the high initial cost, loss of phase-change capabilities, corrosion, and sweating have prevented widespread adoption.

With assistance from the U.S. Department of Energy's Building Technologies Program, Oak Ridge National Laboratory (ORNL) has developed insulation materials that will contribute to reducing energy use in buildings. The insulation materials are enhanced by either spraying with a microencapsulated PCM and adhesive mixture or encapsulating the PCM between two layers of plastic film to form an array of PCM cells. Microencapsulation of the PCM material has eliminated most of the drawbacks of past generation PCMs. Laboratory heat-flow measurements demonstrated that with a 20 wt % PCM content, the heat flow through the insulation was reduced by 30%. The phase change energy transfer (enthalpy) of the PCM is about 40% higher than competitive paraffinic PCMs.

ORNL's research has demonstrated that PCMs can be mixed with fiber insulations, incorporated into structural and sheathing materials, or packaged for localized application. The PCM is nonpetroleum-based, low cost, and flame retardant. The materials can be installed in retrofit applications, e.g., reconstruction of poorly insulated existing attics, or in new construction. The PCM material received a 2009 R&D 100 Award as the first-ever organic, fire-resistant PCM.

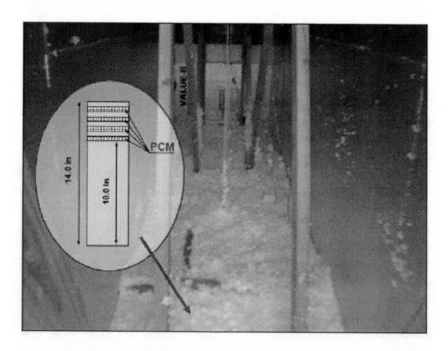

ORNL's Blown PCM Envelope Insulation Material .

Technology History
- Developed by ORNL.
- Commercialized in 2007.
- Available from: Advanced Fiber Technologies

www.advancedfiber.com
Microtek Laboratories
www.microteklabs.com

Applications
Can be used in residential or commercial building applications.

Capabilities
- Improves building energy efficiency by 25–40% compared with Southeast building code levels of insulation.
- Can be installed in existing or new construction.

Benefits

Cost Savings
Uses recycled materials to maintain cost effectiveness and environmental friendliness.

Energy Efficiency
Achieves 30% energy efficiency gain compared with typical insulation material.

Environment
Uses sustainable plant and animal fats.

Safety
Provides fire-resistant PCM for insulation applications.

Contact Information:
Dr. Andre Desjarlais
Email: desjarlaisa@ornl.gov
Phone: (865) 574-9354
Oak Ridge National Laboratory
PO Box 2008, MS-6070 Oak Ridge, TN 37831-6070
Website: http://www.ornl.gov/btric

Echo™: A Hybrid Solar Electric/Thermal System

Innovative System Delivers Energy to Meet Residential Appliance and HVAC Loads

The idea of capturing waste heat from solar photovoltaic (PV) modules is well-developed, and several products based on this concept are currently on the market. However, all of these technologies use water as the working fluid, which creates systemic issues such as high cost, low reliability, and conflict with standard roofing installation practices.

With assistance from the U.S. Department of Energy's Building Technologies Program, PVT Solar, Inc., has developed the Echo™ solar system for residential buildings. The system uses air as its working fluid and employs a patented mounting system to create a seamless rooftop solar array. Air is drawn under the array by a computer-controlled mechanical blower and thermal energy is transferred from the heated solar PV panels to the air. The air is then drawn through a filter and across a heat exchanger, where the thermal energy can be transferred to a variety of uses such as water heating or HVAC. The air-based design also enables nighttime passive cooling via an economizer cycle and radiative cooling to the night sky. An advanced controller governs the system's operation to optimize energy production and direct the thermal energy to the appropriate loads within the home. The system also comes with a web-based user interface so that homeowners can see how their system is performing and adjust system controls from their computer.

PVT Solar's technology is rapidly gaining market acceptance as an advanced and complete solar solution. Echo can offset over 50% of a home's energy needs, helping to move towards energy-efficient building goals. The system was commercially introduced to customers in 2009 and is now standard in multiple new home communities throughout Arizona and Utah. Future development efforts are focused on increasing the efficiency of thermal energy capture and load utilization, as well as using the system's advanced controls to drive total home energy-efficiency measures.

Technology History
- Developed by PVT Solar, Inc.
- Commercialized in 2009, with more than 50 systems installed in the U.S.

Residential Installation of PVT Solar's Echo Solar System.

U.S. Energy Savings (Billion Btu)

Cumulative through 2009	2009
1.71	1.71

U.S. Emissions Reductions (Cumulative Tons)

Particulates	SO_x	NO_x	Carbon
0.01	0.37	0.28	33.61

Applications
Can be used to provide standalone electrical and thermal energy for residential buildings.

Capabilities
- Provides a complete solar energy solution for heating, cooling, hot water, and ventilation.
- Optimizes energy production and delivery to contribute towards meeting energy-efficient building goals.

Benefits

Durability

Achieves a high level of reliability by using an air-based (waterless) design.

Simplicity

Provides a simple design that can be installed using standard roofing practices.

Contact Information:
Gordon Handelsman
Email: ghandelsman@pvtsolar.com
Phone: (805) 427-3752
PVT Solar, Inc.
2607 7th Street, Suite G
Berkeley, CA 94710
Website: http://www.pvtsolar.com

GeoSpring™ Hybrid Water Heater

New Heat Pump Water Heater Uses up to
62% Less Energy than Standard Electric Models

Water heating is the second largest energy expense in U.S. households (behind space heating/cooling). About 40% of the nation's homes are served by storage tank electric water heaters, which consume an average of roughly 4900 kWh annually. Standard electric water heaters are a mature technology, and it is therefore unlikely that significant energy savings can be achieved without fundamentally altering the way stored water is heated.

With assistance from the U.S. Department of Energy's (DOE's) Building Technologies Program, General Electric Company (GE) has developed the GeoSpring hybrid water heater, which uses heat pump technology to transfer heat from the surrounding air to the stored water. This design enables significant energy savings compared with typical electric water heaters, which generate heat using electric resistance elements. DOE testing for appliance EnergyGuide labeling confirmed that the GeoSpring heat pump uses 62% less energy than a standard 50-gallon electric water heater. The GeoSpring offers five different operating modes to adjust to changing hot water demand. For low-demand situations or when maximum energy efficiency is desired, the unit can operate entirely as a heat pump. For high-demand situations, backup resistive elements are used to boost the temperature recovery time to that of a standard electric water heater. The unit can also save energy by lowering the water temperature setpoint during extended periods of time in which a house is unoccupied (e.g., vacation) and returning to the previous setting shortly before the residents return.

GE is currently focused on marketing the product to build consumer awareness of the advantages offered by heat pump water heaters. GeoSpring was the first ENERGY STAR qualified heat pump water heater, and also qualifies for the Federal 30% residential energy efficiency tax credit and numerous State and local utility rebates/incentives. The product is currently available through several national retailers, local independent retailers, and local plumbers and plumbing distributors.

GE's GeoSpring Hybrid Residential Water Heater.

Technology History
- Developed by General Electric Company and commercialized in 2009.
- First ENERGY STAR qualified heat pump water heater.

U.S. Energy Savings (Billion Btu)

Cumulative through 2009	2009
68.2	68.2

U.S. Emissions Reductions (Cumulative Tons)

Particulates	SO$_x$	NO$_x$	Carbon
0.14	7.48	9.28	1202

Applications
Can be used as an energy-efficient alternative to standard residential electric water heaters.

Capabilities
- Offers a capacity of 50 gallons, a first hour rating of 63 gallons, and an energy factor of 2.35 when in hybrid mode.
- Provides demand response readiness and communicates with a smart meter or power utility load controller.

Benefits

Compatibility
Retrofits easily by using the same utility connections as standard electric water heaters.

Cost Savings
Saves the average U.S. household $300 per year on its electric bills compared with a standard electric water heater.

Contact Information:
Keith Burkhardt
Email: Keith.Burkhardt@ge.com
Phone: (502) 452-4084
GE Company
GE Appliance Park, AP4-255
Louisville, KY 40225
Website: http://www.ge.com

NextAire™ Packaged Gas Heat Pump

Rooftop Heat Pump Provides Low-Cost Space Conditioning for Commercial Buildings

Commercial buildings in the U.S. are predominantly cooled and heated using packaged rooftop HVAC units, most of which use an electric-motor-driven compressor to drive the refrigeration cycle. Unfortunately, the operating cost of these electric units can be very high due to expensive demand and time-of-use electricity prices. In addition, the high summertime peak electricity demand for space cooling puts stress on regional electrical grids and necessitates an excess of generation capacity that is underutilized during off-peak hours. An alternative source of power for operating space conditioning equipment is needed.

With assistance from the U.S. Department of Energy's (DOE's) Building Technologies Program and the U.S. Department of Defense, IntelliChoice Energy has developed the NextAire 11-ton packaged gas heat pump (PGHP). The PGHP uses a natural-gas-fired engine (instead of an electric motor) to drive its pair of scroll compressors. The unit's efficiency is enhanced in heating mode by its ability to capture and use waste heat from the engine for space heating. In addition, the engine can operate at variable speeds to enable efficient operation at part load conditions. Many electric heat pumps are constrained to operating at full capacity, which can result in cycling losses from repeated startups and shutdowns after quickly meeting a small heating or cooling demand. The PGHP is well-suited for new commercial construction or retrofit applications because it occupies a similar footprint to traditional electric units currently in use.

Widespread use of the gas heat pump technology has the potential to result in large energy efficiency and resource conservation gains on the national level. According to the U.S. Energy Information Administration, more than

60% of the primary energy consumed to generate the nation's electricity is lost in power plants during the conversion process. Shifting a significant fraction of commercial space conditioning to natural gas would avoid these conversion losses and the large amounts of water consumed during electricity generation.

IntelliChoice Energy's 11-ton NextAire PGHP.

Technology History
- Developed by IntelliChoice Energy, with assistance from Southwest Gas Corporation and Oak Ridge National Laboratory.
- Commercialized in 2010 by IntelliChoice Energy, with 50 units sold and installed in the U.S.
- Received a 2010 New Product Award from the National Society of Professional Engineers.

Applications
Can be used to provide low-cost, energy-efficient space conditioning for commercial buildings.

Capabilities
- Uses a natural-gas-fired engine (instead of an electric motor) to drive refrigerant compressors.
- Provides 11 tons of cooling/heating capacity with a cooling coefficient of performance (COP) of 1.1 and a heating COP of 1.4.
- Captures waste heat from the engine to increase efficiency in heating mode.

Benefits

Cost Savings
Reduces operating costs by avoiding expensive demand and time-of-use electricity charges.

Water Savings
Saves 0.5 gallons of water per kWh compared with similar-sized electric units consuming grid-generated electricity.

```
Contact Information:
Sarah Silver
Email: ssilver
Phone: (623) 879-4664 x70206
IntelliChoice Energy
2355 W. Utopia Rd
Phoenix, AZ 85027
Website: http://www.iceghp.com/
```

Quiet Climate 2: Efficient Heat Pump for Portable Classrooms

New Heat Pump Improves Indoor Air
Quality and Reduces Noise in Portable Classrooms
Conventional HVAC systems in portable classrooms suffer from low energy efficiency, poor ventilation, and high noise levels. Ventilation rates in portable classrooms often do not meet the current minimum rate of 15 cubic feet per minute (CFM) per occupant established by the American Society of Heating, Refrigerating and Air-Conditioning Engineers (ASHRAE). In addition, HVAC-related noise levels are often well above the 45 decibel (dB) maximum for unoccupied portable classrooms set by the Collaborative on High Performance Schools. To provide the best possible environment for student and teacher performance, an improved HVAC system that addresses these issues is needed.

With assistance from the U.S. Department of Energy's (DOE's) Building Technologies Program and the California Energy Commission, Lawrence Berkeley National Laboratory (LBNL) and Bard Manufacturing Company, Inc., developed the Quiet Climate 2 heat pump for portable classrooms. The Quiet Climate 2 uses a built-in sound-reducing plenum to achieve operation at an audible noise level of ≤ 42 dB, and can be fitted with additional accessories (sound/vibration curbs and supply/return air acoustical plenums) to further reduce noise levels. The unit delivers the ASHRAE-standard 15 CFM of ventilation air per occupant, which reduces indoor concentrations of carbon dioxide (CO_2), volatile organic compounds, and aldehydes compared with conventional portable classroom HVAC systems. A CO_2 sensor can be added to the unit to enable ventilation control based on the measured CO_2 level within the room. Because of the improvements it offers to the classroom environment, the Quiet Climate 2 was named one of the Top 20 Products in 2009 by *School Construction News*.

Bard's Quiet Climate 2 Heat Pump.

Technology History

- Developed by LBNL and Bard Manufacturing Company, Inc.
- Commercialized in 2008 by Bard and available from regional HVAC distributors.
- Currently being used in several schools throughout the United States.

Applications

Can be used to provide quiet, energy-efficient space conditioning and improved indoor air quality for portable classrooms.

Capabilities

- Provides 3 to 5 tons of cooling/heating capacity with an integrated part-load value (IPLV) of 13.6 to 14.5.
- Reduces audible noise levels to $\leq$ 42 dB while operating and $\leq$ 35 dB while in fan-only mode for ventilation.
- Delivers 480 CFM of ventilation air, or 15 CFM per occupant in a 32-person classroom.

Benefits

Efficiency

Increases efficiency compared with conventional 12 to 13 seasonal energy efficiency ratio (SEER) heat pumps commonly used in portable classrooms.

Indoor Air Quality

Reduces indoor concentrations of CO_2, volatile organic compounds, and aldehydes.

Contact Information:

Paul Quigley

Email: paul.quigley@bardhvac.com

Phone: (419) 636-1194, ext. 364

Bard Manufacturing Company, Inc.

1914 Randolph Drive, P.O. Box 607

Bryan, Ohio 43506

Website: http://www.bardhvac.com/

Vertex™ Residential Gas Condensing Water Heater

Improved Water Heater Design Increases
Thermal Energy Efficiency and Reduces Costs

Water heating accounts for 14% of residential energy consumption. High-efficiency water heaters tend to be much more expensive than traditional products and have lengthy payback periods. The higher cost arises from the use of complex designs that are difficult to manufacture and require expensive materials and components. Poor payback and reliability problems have made these products unappealing to consumers. A cost-optimized, high-efficiency water heater is needed.

With assistance from the U.S. Department of Energy's Building Technologies Program, A.O. Smith Corporation has developed a high-efficiency water heater that addresses the concerns of cost and reliability. The design uses readily available components and materials that reduce the unit cost premium. In addition to the use of standard water heater parts, a glass-lined carbon steel heat exchanger was also developed. The cost savings realized from this choice of heat exchanger material versus stainless steel are significant and simplify manufacturing.

A.O. Smith refined the design specifications for this water heater based on numerous marketing studies and customer input. The design was then further modified to address ease of manufacturing concerns and weaknesses identified during reliability testing. A.O. Smith commercialized the technology in the second quarter of 2006 with the release of the Vertex product family. The first production model had 90% thermal efficiency and a second, with 96% efficiency, was released two years later. Known as the Vertex 100, this newer model has additional features such as on-board diagnostics and remote monitoring capabilities, as well as an upgraded temperature controller with a liquid crystal display user interface.

A.O. Smith's Vertex Product Line of Residential Gas Water Heaters.

Technology History
- Available from A.O. Smith Corporation.
- Commercialized in 2006.

Applications
Can be used for residential or light commercial applications.

Capabilities
- Achieves up to 96% thermal efficiency with an input heating rate of up to 100,000 Btu/h.
- Operates as part of combination space heating/water heating systems.
- Offers a capacity of 50 gallons and a first hour rating of up to 164 gallons.
- Produces hot water at a rate that exceeds that of a standard 75 gallon unit.

Benefits

Compatibility
Installs easily using existing utility connections and can be vented using PVC pipe.

Durability
Provides reliable performance by using a field-tested design.

Energy Savings
Achieves up to 30% energy savings compared with a standard gas water heater.

Contact Information:
Kim Laurette
Email: klaurette@hotwater.com
Phone: (519) 787-5527
A.O. Smith Corporation
500 Tennessee Waltz Pkwy.
Ashland City, TN 37105
Website: http://www.hotwater.com

High-Efficiency LED Lamp for Solid-State Lighting

LED Emitter Increases Light Output and Reduces Manufacturing Costs

Lighting accounts for roughly 20% of total U.S. electricity consumption. Energy-efficient lighting technologies can therefore have a large impact on reducing the nation's energy consumption and greenhouse gas emissions. Solid-state light-emitting diodes (LEDs) have recently emerged as a viable new light source, with much greater efficiency than traditional lighting technologies (e.g., incandescent and halogen lighting). However, LED performance, durability, and color rendering still needs to be improved in order for large-scale adoption of the technology to occur.

White LEDs are mainly produced by combining a blue-emitting nitride-based LED with yellow-emitting phosphor materials, such as cerium-doped yttrium aluminum garnet. In the past, the performance of white LEDs for lighting applications was limited to about 50 lm/W. Given the relative cost of white LEDs, such performance levels were insufficient to challenge the incumbent lighting technologies. However, Cree, Inc., has developed blue EZBright® LED power chip technology, which enables lighting-class white LED products with efficacies of more than 100 lm/W. Continuing development by Cree has since increased the performance as high as 120 lm/W for cool white and 92 lm/W for warm white LEDs (based on commercially available EZBright LED chips).

Cree's EZBright LEDs combine highly efficient indium gallium nitride materials with proprietary optical design and device submount technology. The entire product family incorporates or builds on technology that was developed in part with funding provided by the U.S. Department of Energy's Building Technologies Program. The chip's optical design maximizes light extraction efficiency and enables a Lambertian radiation pattern, while the thin, vertical structure enables low forward voltage and efficient heat dissipation.

Technology History

- Available from Cree, Inc.
- Commercialized in 2006.
- Continuing development to increase cool and warm white high-power LED performance.

Applications

Can be used for a broad range of applications, including general illumination, automotive lighting, and consumer mobile products.

Cree Lighting CR6 Downlight with EZBright Die (inset).

Capabilities

- Achieves an efficacy of up to 120 lm/W when combined with suitable phosphors and packaging materials.
- Achieves die level power output of more than 380 mW at 350 mA drive current and 850 mW at 1 A drive current in the range of 450 – 460 nm.

Benefits

Cost Savings

Offers compatibility with low-cost phosphor application processes, which simplifies white LED manufacturing.

Energy Savings

Increases lighting efficacy by up to 10 times compared with incandescent light bulbs.

Versatility
Enables customization of device geometry for use in varying applications.

Contact Information: Monica Hansen *Email:* monica_hansen@cree.com *Phone:* (805) 690-3032 Cree, Inc. 4600 Silicon Drive Durham, NC 27703 Website: http://www.cree.com/

Integrated, Solid-State LED Luminaire for General Lighting

Longer-Lasting, LED-Based Lighting Replaces Conventional Lamps

Light-emitting diodes (LEDs) have recently emerged as a viable new light source, with demonstrated efficiency levels up to 10 times that of traditional lighting technologies. The lighting industry could benefit greatly from energy-efficient lighting solutions, especially in spotlighting applications. A highly efficient, durable, and inexpensive spotlight is needed that can provide aesthetically pleasing illumination with a uniform beam pattern. Such a device would need to retain common form factors and accommodate existing hardware, sockets, and power connections.

With assistance from the U.S. Department of Energy's Building Technologies Program, Philips Color Kinetics has developed an LED-based parabolic aluminum reflector (PAR) lamp with a standard form factor that allows the lamp to be used with existing lighting fixtures. The lamp contains a compact power supply and novel electronic control for operating high-intensity LEDs, as well as a heat sink for thermal management and optics for producing the desired beam. The concept lamp developed under this program used LEDs of different colors to produce warm white light with good color rendering. The lamp was designed to have a life expectancy of at least 35,000 hours, with an efficacy ≥ 40 lumens per watt (lm/W) and a color rendering index ≥ 90.

Philips Color Kinetics' technology was entered into the L-Prize competition, a DOE-sponsored contest for developing an LED-based 60 W incandescent and PAR 38 halogen bulb replacement. The Philips submittal was the first entry received and was recognized by *Time* magazine as one of the 50 Best Inventions of 2009. Philips has commercially introduced a complete family of LED PAR lamps, A-lamps, and decorative lamps for professional and residential applications, all using the technology developed under this DOE project. In addition, Philips Color Kinetics has introduced LED cove lighting and outdoor flood lighting using this technology. Philips continues to develop and improve SSL product performance, including meeting new ENERGY STAR criteria.

Philips 12W A19 Ambient LED™ and eW Cove MX Powercore.

Technology History

- Available from Philips Lighting.
- Commercialized in 2009.
- Continuing development to meet ENERGY STAR criteria.

Applications
Can be used for a broad range of commercial and residential lighting applications.

Capabilities
- Achieves up to 64 lm/W in a 60 W equivalent LED A-lamp.
- Produces soft white light and is fully dimmable.

Benefits

Durability
Provides up to 25,000 hours of useful life for LED A-lamps, and 50,000+ hours for LED cove lights.

Efficiency
Achieves an 80% gain in energy efficiency compared with industry standard A-lamp equivalents.

Environment
Does not contain mercury or give off an excessive amount of heat. Does not emit color-fading ultraviolet light and is safe for use around colored artwork and upholstery.

> Contact Information:
> James Anderson
> *Email:* jim.anderson@philips.com
> *Phone:* (781) 418-9306
> Philips Color Kinetics
> 3 Burlington Woods Burlington, MA 01803
> Website: http://www.lighting.philips.com

Adapting Wireless Technology for Lighting Control

Cost-Effective, Advanced System Control Reduces Energy Consumption
The high cost of retrofitting buildings with advanced lighting control systems hinders more widespread use of this technology. The energy-saving and occupant comfort benefits of advanced lighting control have not been realized on a large scale because of the cost and difficulty of installing and commissioning electronic dimmable ballasts and supporting hardware. Retrofitting existing buildings with dimmable ballasts and appropriate sensors requires running new control wires, which makes the cost and complexity of installing such systems prohibitive. Wireless technology offers a solution to mounting installation costs because it requires no additional wiring. Cost-effective, low-power, low-data-rate wireless networking devices could reduce the barriers to implementing advanced lighting control and provide reliable

transmission of remote sensor data and control commands to and from remote system components.

With assistance from the U.S. Department of Energy's Building Technologies Program, ELB Electronics, Inc., and industry partners have developed advanced wireless controls for lighting applications. The system consists of a network of wireless-controllable actuators, electronic dimmable lamp ballasts, and sensors for light level and occupancy detection. The system can monitor and control the lighting network by computer software, which was developed to implement advanced lighting control algorithms, including daylighting, occupancy control, and demand response.

Based on standard industry practices, an analysis estimated that the installation cost of a wireless advanced lighting control system for a retrofit application is at least 30% lower than a comparable wired system for a typical 16,000 square-foot office building, with a payback period of less than 3 years. Occupants will benefit from improved workplace comfort; building owners will benefit from improved energy efficiency and flexible lighting control; and utilities will benefit from energy savings that are responsive to peak demand periods. Commercial lighting consumes approximately 3.7 quad per year. A 35% long-term market penetration with an average of 40% energy savings could save 0.52 quad annually from using advanced lighting control strategies.

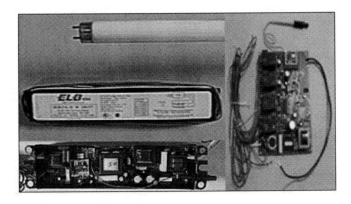

ELB's Wireless Dimmer, Ballast, and Relay Modules.

Technology History
- Developed by ELB Electronics, Inc.
- Commercialized in 2007.
- Continuing development with Zigbee™ communication capabilities.

Applications
Can be used in commercial, retail and educational building applications.

Capabilities
- Provides localized control and centralized programmable monitoring and control for entire lighting system.
- Reduces energy consumption by monitoring use, demand, and occupancy and by integrating daylighting schemes.
- Achieves full-range dimming in electronic fluorescent lamp ballasts.

Benefits

Cost Savings
Improves return on investment by reducing installation cost of lighting control systems.

Durability
Meets UL and ANSI industry standard test specifications for safety and performance.

Flexibility
Supports small scale to entire building installations and can be reconfigured to changes in space utilization.

Installation
Provides a cost-effective, drop-in, retrofit solution that is designed to be compatible with existing lighting components.

Contact Information:
Steven Purdy
Email: spurdy@elbelectronics.com
Phone: (626) 446-5852
ELB Electronics, Inc.
67 E. Live Oak Avenue, Suite 101
Arcadia, CA 91006
Website: http://www.elbelectronics.com

Ballast/Driver Technology for Metal Halide or Solid-State Lighting Systems

Energy-Efficient Power Control Circuit Improves Lamp Performance

New energy-efficient accent lighting systems must overcome the challenge of providing adequate performance (instant-start and light levels) compared with incandescent-based systems at a competitive first cost. Compact fluorescent lamps are not suitable for accent lighting because of their low light output and delayed start. Metal halide (MH) lamps have adequate light output, but do not start instantly and cannot be scaled to very low wattages, resulting in higher system costs.

With the assistance of a U.S. Department of Energy Small Business Innovation Research grant, Energy Focus, Inc., tackled the major performance challenges in existing accent lighting systems. Energy Focus developed a lamp ballast technology that achieves the instant-on operation of a low-power MH-lampbased accent lighting system. The technology works by incorporating efficient topologies for lamp ignition, power-factor-corrected (PFC) power conversion, and constant-current regulation. Optimized lamp start-up and operation is achieved by programmable control of the lamp current. This work led to the development of Energy Focus's next-generation constant-current lightemitting-diode (LED) driver, which increases the reliability of solid-state lighting (SSL) products.

The ballast technology is currently used in Energy Focus's MH-based products, and in fixtures that have passed military specification testing for shock, vibration, and electrical surge conditions. The military-qualified SSL fixtures are in production and include berth lights, general lighting fixtures, and globe lights. SSL-based explosion-proof fixtures are currently under development for military and NASA applications. Future LED driver electronics based on this technology could include wireless enabled, individually addressable, networked drivers or fixtures.

Technology History
- Available from Energy Focus, Inc.
- Commercialized in 2009.
- Currently developing SSL products for general and hazardous environment lighting applications.

Applications
Can be used in MH- and SSL-based lighting systems.

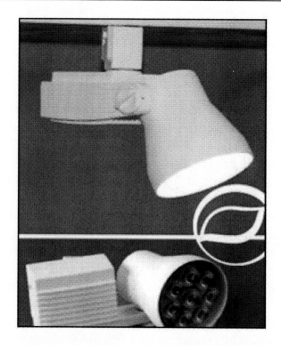

Energy Focus's SSL Tracklight Fixture .

Capabilities
- Provides instant-start operation.
- Enables advanced power factor correction with low total harmonic distortion and efficient constant-current control.
- Provides 92% efficient ballast circuitry, which improves the efficacy (lumens per watt) of lighting systems.

Benefits

Durability
Achieves military specifications for harsh environments. Units have operated in the field for more than three years without experiencing a single failure.

Efficiency
Achieves an 80% gain in energy efficiency relative to existing incandescent/halogen systems.

Contact Information:
Roger Buelow
Email: rbuelow@efoi.com
Phone: (440) 715-1251
Energy Focus, Inc.
32000 Aurora Road
Solon, Ohio 44139
Website: http://www.energyfocusinc.com

SageGlass® Electrochromic Windows

***Daylighting-Compatible, Electronically
Tinting Glass Reduces HVAC Solar Loading***

For centuries, buildings have had windows because people desire the natural daylight that windows provide. Unfortunately, windows permit heat to escape from a building in the winter and enter in the summer, and allow glare to penetrate into a building's interior. Buildings account for approximately 70% of U.S. electricity consumption and 40% of the nation's total energy use. Technologies that reduce energy transmission through windows can therefore have a significant impact towards reducing the nation's energy consumption and greenhouse gas emissions. Many window treatments for reducing solar loading and glare, such as shades and blinds, also eliminate natural daylight and the building occupants' sense of connection to the outside, counteracting the purpose of the windows.

With assistance from the U.S. Department of Energy's Building Technologies Program, SAGE Electrochromics, Inc., has developed a window glazing technology that overcomes conventional window insulation challenges and preserves the benefits of natural daylighting. SAGE's electrochromic glass technology consists of a series of ceramic layers on glass that can be either clear or tinted by applying low-voltage DC electricity. Clear SageGlass transmits 62% of visible light and has a solar heat gain coefficient (fraction of solar radiation admitted through a window) of 0.48. When the window is tinted, the light transmission drops to 3.5% with a solar heat gain coefficient of 0.09. The average SageGlass glazing energy consumption is only 0.4 W per m^2 (10 ft^2). In relative terms, a single 60 W light bulb's electricity consumption would operate 1500 ft^2 of SageGlass.

In northern climates, the glazing technology has the potential to conserve energy by allowing passive solar irradiation to supplement heating and by harvesting daylight to augment (or replace) artificial lighting. For warmer climates, fully darkened SageGlass glazing can significantly reduce both air conditioning loads and peak power consumption. Even when in the tinted state, SAGE's glazing technology permits building occupants to view the outdoors, a feature that is beneficial to people's well-being and productivity.

SageGlass Glazing Installation Demonstrating Clear and Tinted States .

Technology History
- Developed and marketed by SAGE Electrochromics, Inc.
- Commercialized in 2007.

U.S. Energy Savings (Billion Btu)

Cumulative through 2009	Cumulative through 2009
2.23	1.16

U.S. Emissions Reductions (Cumulative Tons)

Particulates	SO$_x$	NO$_x$	Carbon
0.01	0.48	0.36	43.74

Applications
Can be used to control transmission of the sun's light and heat through windows, thereby reducing building HVAC solar loading.

Capabilities
- Transitions between clear and tinted states within 3-5 minutes.
- Offers zone-based tinting control so that certain window panels block the sun's direct glare while others allow natural daylight to enter a room.

Benefits

Comfort

Blocks glare without compromising visibility and reduces sunlight fading damage to interior décor.

Versatility

Offers a variety of tint colors to suit consumer preferences for differing applications in both residential and commercial buildings.

Contact Information:
Neil Sbar
Email: nsbar@sage-ec.com
Phone: (877) 724-3321
SAGE Electrochromics, Inc.
One Sage Way
Faribault, MN 55021
Website: http://www.sage-ec.com

APPENDIX D: EMERGING TECHNOLOGY DESCRIPTIONS

Insulating Form System for Concrete Foundation Edges

Innovative Technology Reduces Heat
Loss through Slab-on-Grade Foundations

Concrete slab-on-grade construction represents the primary foundation type of residential buildings throughout the southern and southwestern United States. Almost all of these homes have uninsulated slab perimeters that transfer heat from the warm interior of the house to the surrounding environment during the heating season. Builders currently have the opportunity to install slab edge insulation on new homes, but typically choose not to do so. Factors that influence their decision include added cost, installation difficulties, construction slowdown, and termite issues (in some parts of the country). A cost-effective, installer-friendly slab edge insulation system would offer multiple benefits to builders and homeowners, while reducing the energy consumption and greenhouse gas emissions associated with residential buildings.

With assistance from the U.S. Department of Energy's Building Technologies Program, Davis Energy Group, Inc. (DEG), is developing Formsulate, a leavein-place concrete slab form board. Formsulate consists of a PVC extrusion filled with two inches of Styrofoam™ insulation, along with specialized linear and corner couplers. Formsulate decreases construction labor by eliminating the need to strip form boards after the concrete has cured. The wooden form boards historically used in the slab-forming process end up as waste material and typically add an additional 400 pounds of construction waste per house. Formsulate eliminates this source of waste while allowing concrete subcontractors to continue using industry-standard forming practices. The insulation reduces heat loss through concrete slab edges, especially in homes with hydronic floor heating systems. In addition, the insulation is treated with approved termite-resistant chemicals to prevent termites from tunneling through the foam into the wall framing above.

DEG has conducted two field demonstrations using the Formsulate form boards to pour slab-on-grade foundations for custom homes in California. Future R&D work involves developing a Formsulate design that is compatible with post-tensioned concrete slabs.

Innovative Technology Reduces Heat Loss through Slab-on-Grade Foundations

Concrete slab-on-grade construction represents the primary foundation type of residential buildings throughout the southern and southwestern United States. Almost all of these homes have uninsulated slab perimeters that transfer heat from the warm interior of the house to the surrounding environment during the heating season. Builders currently have the opportunity to install slab edge insulation on new homes, but typically choose not to do so. Factors that influence their decision include added cost, installation difficulties, construction slowdown, and termite issues (in some parts of the country). A cost-effective, installer-friendly slab edge insulation system would offer multiple benefits to builders and homeowners, while reducing the energy consumption and greenhouse gas emissions associated with residential buildings.

With assistance from the U.S. Department of Energy's Building Technologies Program, Davis Energy Group, Inc. (DEG), is developing Formsulate, a leavein-place concrete slab form board. Formsulate consists of a PVC extrusion filled with two inches of Styrofoam™ insulation, along with specialized linear and corner couplers. Formsulate decreases construction labor by eliminating the need to strip form boards after the concrete has cured. The wooden form boards historically used in the slab-forming process end up as waste material and typically add an additional 400 pounds of construction waste per house. Formsulate eliminates this source of waste while allowing concrete subcontractors to continue using industry-standard forming practices. The insulation reduces heat loss through concrete slab edges, especially in homes with hydronic floor heating systems. In addition, the insulation is treated with approved termite-resistant chemicals to prevent termites from tunneling through the foam into the wall framing above.

DEG has conducted two field demonstrations using the Formsulate form boards to pour slab-on-grade foundations for custom homes in California. Future R&D work involves developing a Formsulate design that is compatible with post-tensioned concrete slabs.

Field Demonstration of DEG's Formsulate Technology.

Technology History

- Developed by DEG, in partnership with The Dow Chemical Company and with support from the National Energy Technology Laboratory.
- Planning to develop a Formsulate design that can be used with post-tensioned concrete slabs.

Applications

Can be used as an energy-saving alternative to conventional wooden form boards in the process of forming concrete slabs for residential buildings.

Capabilities

- Reduces heat loss through concrete slab edges by more than 80% compared with uninsulated slab-on-grade foundations.
- Offers twelve-foot-long linear extrusions, linear couplers, and both internal and external corner couplers.

Benefits

Emissions Reductions

Reduces greenhouse gas emissions by lowering building heating loads.

Safety

Prevents termites from tunneling through the insulation and causing structural damage to the wall framing.

Waste Reduction

Reduces construction waste by eliminating the scrap wood resulting from use of traditional wooden form boards.

Contact Information:
Marc Hoeschele
Email: mhoesch@davisenergy.com
Phone: (530) 753-1100, ext. 23
Davis Energy Group, Inc.
123 C Street Davis, CA 95616
Website: http://www.davisenergy.com

Three-Dimensional Building Energy Performance Measurement and Modeling System

New Technology Improves Building Envelope Retrofit Decision Making

Many homeowners or building owners trying to improve the energy performance of their building envelopes are faced with choosing from a large number of products and services with widely differing applications, initial costs, and payback periods. Making sense of this large amount of complex information can be difficult for individuals without any formal training or education regarding the energy performance of building components. A need exists for technologies and information dissemination methods that will help the general public make informed retrofit decisions that reduce energy losses through their walls, roofs, windows, and doors.

With assistance from the U.S. Department of Energy's Building Technologies Program, the University of Nebraska-Lincoln's Durham School of Architectural Engineering and Construction is developing a technology that improves the measurement and modeling of building envelope energy performance. The system measures thermal radiation from envelope materials and uses light detection and ranging (LIDAR) technology to generate a three-dimensional (3D) model that stores thermal performance information at each point in space. After further analysis and information modeling, the University will deliver the final 3D model to building owners and homeowners via the internet.

Compared with numerical and graphical data, visual information about a building's energy performance is easier for nonexperts to understand. The ability to actually see thermal performance deficiencies in a building's envelope will help homeowners identify retrofit technologies that will have the greatest impact on reducing their energy consumption and monthly energy bills. The technology will also help the scientific community quickly and accurately gather building thermal performance data for use in additional modeling and analysis efforts.

Technology History
- Developed by the University of Nebraska-Lincoln's Durham School of Architectural Engineering and Construction.
- Currently conducting lab and field experiments to test an algorithm for estimating the thermal resistance of building envelope materials.

Applications

Can be used to rapidly and accurately measure building envelope thermal conditions for further analysis and modeling, the results of which can be disseminated to building owners and managers via the internet.

3D Thermal Modeling of a House Performed by theUniversity of Nebraska's Hybrid Thermal LIDAR System.

Capabilities

- Integrates 3D geometries of a building's envelope with thermal resistance information for the envelope materials (e.g., walls, roofs, windows, and doors).
- Stores thermal performance information at each point in 3D space.
- Delivers model results to homeowners and building owners via the internet.

Benefits

Energy Savings

Informs the public about techniques for improving the energy efficiency of their homes and buildings.

Simplicity
Offers visual information about a building's energy performance, which is easier for nonexperts (e.g., homeowners) to understand.

Contact Information:
Dr. Yong K. Cho
Email: ycho2@unl.edu
Phone: (402) 554-3277
University of Nebraska-Lincoln
1110 South 67th St.
Peter Kiewit Institute-104C
Omaha, NE 68182-0816
Website: http://www.engineering.unl.edu

Accurate Feed-Forward Temperature Control for Tankless Water Heaters

New Algorithm Improves Temperature Control in Tankless Water Heaters

Water heating accounts for 14% of primary energy use in the residential sector of the U.S. economy, or about 3 quads of energy per year. The current water heater market is dominated by traditional tank-style heaters, which accounted for 97% of all units sold in 2006. All tank-style heaters suffer from standby losses, which is the continual loss of heat through the walls of the tank to the surrounding environment. Tankless water heaters (TWHs) eliminate the energy penalty of standby losses by heating water only as it is being used instead of storing heated water in a tank. Despite this benefit, TWHs have a very small market share (about 3%) due to a number of drawbacks. One important issue is the inability of many TWHs to maintain a desired outlet temperature across the rapidly changing flowrates common in residential water heating systems.

With assistance from the U.S. Department of Energy's Building Technologies Program, Building Solutions, Inc. (BSI), developed an improved method of temperature control for electric TWHs. Conventional systems rely only on feedback control, whereby the water outlet temperature is compared to the setpoint and the controller adjusts power to the heating element to eliminate any difference between the two values. BSI used a control algorithm that incorporates both feedback and feed-forward control. By comparing the setpoint to the temperature of water entering the heater (feed-forward control), power to the heating element can be pre-adjusted to provide outlet water at the appropriate temperature. BSI's control algorithm results in faster convergence to the setpoint and an improved ability to maintain the water outlet temperature at the setpoint.

A prototype TWH using BSI's control algorithm was developed that offers many improvements over currently available heaters, including a modular design for easy scalability. BSI is currently seeking a partnership with a water heater manufacturer to commercialize the control technology.

BSI's User Interface Controller for TWHs.

Technology History
- Developed by BSI.
- Currently seeking a partnership with a water heater manufacturing company to commercialize the technology.

Applications
Can be used to provide improved temperature control for TWHs in various applications (e.g., whole-house water heating, restaurant kitchens, industrial applications, and point-of-use showers or faucets).

Capabilities
- Improves the ability of TWHs to maintain a specified outlet temperature and quickly respond to changing flowrates.
- Spreads electric load evenly over time to avoid the flickering of lights in a home caused by rapid voltage fluctuations in conventional TWHs.

Benefits

Adaptability
Uses a modular design for easy construction of different capacity heaters, enabling use of the TWH as a booster heater for solar and heat pump water heaters.

Energy Savings
Offers a small size that enables point-ofuse water heating, significantly reducing the distribution losses associated with conventional water heaters.

Safety
Can be programmed with fault detection and diagnosis routines to increase safety and enable easier maintenance.

```
Contact Information:
David Yuill
Email: david@bsiengineering.com
Phone: (402) 556-3382
Building Solutions, Inc.
3315 S. 96th St.
Omaha, NE 68124
Website: http://www.bsiengineering.com/
```

AIR BEARING HEAT EXCHANGER

Novel Air-Cooled Heat Exchanger Improves Efficiency and Performance of HVAC Equipment

Air-cooled heat exchanger technology has changed so little in the past half century that its role in determining the efficiency, reliability, and net carbon footprint of the nation's energy infrastructure has largely been forgotten. Air conditioners, heat pumps, and refrigeration equipment comprise 24% of the load on our nation's electrical grid. A breakthrough in air-cooled heat exchanger technology could significantly reduce this figure. The electricity demand spikes imposed by cooling loads are also very detrimental to grid reliability and operating margin. Advances in air-cooled heat exchanger technology should therefore be a central tenet of any grid-surety strategy.

With assistance from the U.S. Department of Energy's Building Technologies Program, Sandia National Laboratories (SNL) is developing air bearing heat exchanger technology. In this novel device, heat is transferred across a narrow air gap from a stationary heat spreader to a rotating structure that is a hybrid of a finned heat sink and an impeller. This configuration places the heat sink boundary layer in an accelerating frame of reference, which at several thousand rpm, reduces the thickness of the boundary layer by up to 10 times, thereby greatly enhancing heat transfer.

The device's "direct drive" architecture generates relative motion between the finned heat sink and surrounding air by simply rotating the heat-sink-impeller through the air. This design significantly improves efficiency and reduces fan noise. While conventional fans suffer from limited aerodynamic efficiencies, all of the shaft work provided by the motor of the air bearing heat exchanger is used to create relative motion between the heat sink and the surrounding air. The rotating finned structure is also the first air-cooled heat exchanger device architecture with intrinsic immunity to heat sink fouling. Dust and other foreign matter entering the intake of conventional air-cooled heat exchangers cause severe performance degradation over time. In contrast, these particles do not adhere to the rapidly rotating heat-sink-impeller structure.

Air-cooled heat exchanger technology has changed so little in the past half century that its role in determining the efficiency, reliability, and net carbon footprint of the nation's energy infrastructure has largely been forgotten. Air conditioners, heat pumps, and refrigeration equipment comprise 24% of the load on our nation's electrical grid. A breakthrough in air-cooled heat exchanger technology could significantly reduce this figure. The electricity demand spikes imposed by cooling loads are also very detrimental to grid reliability and operating margin. Advances in air-cooled heat exchanger technology should therefore be a central tenet of any grid-surety strategy.

With assistance from the U.S. Department of Energy's Building Technologies Program, Sandia National Laboratories (SNL) is developing air bearing heat exchanger technology. In this novel device, heat is transferred across a narrow air gap from a stationary heat spreader to a rotating structure that is a hybrid of a finned heat sink and an impeller. This configuration places the heat sink boundary layer in an accelerating frame of reference, which at several thousand rpm, reduces the thickness of the boundary layer by up to 10 times, thereby greatly enhancing heat transfer.

The device's "direct drive" architecture generates relative motion between the finned heat sink and surrounding air by simply rotating the heat-sink-impeller through the air. This design significantly improves efficiency and reduces fan noise. While conventional fans suffer from limited aerodynamic efficiencies, all of the shaft work provided by the motor of the air bearing heat exchanger is used to create relative motion between the heat sink and the surrounding air. The rotating finned structure is also the first air-cooled heat exchanger device architecture with intrinsic immunity to heat sink fouling. Dust and other foreign matter entering the intake of conventional air-cooled heat exchangers cause severe performance degradation over time. In contrast, these particles do not adhere to the rapidly rotating heat-sink-impeller structure.

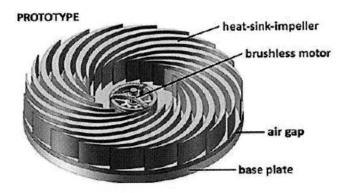

SNL's Prototype Air Bearing Heat Exchanger .

Technology History
- Developed by SNL.
- Demonstrated Version 1.0 prototype in July 2009.
- Continuing to optimize fluid dynamics and determine device scaling laws.

Applications
Can be used to improve the efficiency and performance of HVAC equipment such as air conditioners, heat pumps, refrigerators, and computer processor fans.

Capabilities
- Increases volumetric cooling capacity by 10 times relative to conventional fan and finned heat sink systems.
- Reduces the amount of audible noise generated during cooling compared with fans.
- Eliminates the common problem of heat sink fouling through rapid rotation of the heat-sink-impeller.

Benefits

Efficiency
Maximizes productive translation of mechanical work into relative motion between the heat sink and the surrounding air, while simultaneously reducing audible noise.

Performance
Improves heat transfer by placing the thermal boundary layer in an accelerating reference frame.

Contact Information:
Dr. Jeff Koplow
Email: jkoplow@sandia.gov
Phone: (925) 294-2458
Sandia National Laboratories
BLDG 905, RM 122
Livermore, CA 94550
Website: http://www.sandia.gov/

AMMONIA ABSORPTION TECHNOLOGIES FOR HVAC SYSTEMS

Innovative Technologies Provide Energy-Efficient Absorption Space Conditioning

Absorption air conditioning systems, which use heat instead of an electric-motor-driven compressor to drive the refrigeration cycle, offer several advantages compared with conventional vapor-compression systems. Absorption systems use ammonia as the refrigerant, which has a higher heat of vaporization than fluorocarbons and does not have any ozone-depletion or global warming potential. Absorption systems also have fewer moving parts than vapor-compression systems, which increases product lifetime. Despite these advantages, the market penetration of absorption HVAC technologies has been limited by their low level of efficiency.

With assistance from the U.S. Department of Energy's Building Technologies Program, Rocky Research is developing new technologies that will increase the efficiency of absorption systems. One important innovation is the use of generator-absorber heat exchange, which captures heat given off by the absorption of ammonia to help drive the distillation of ammonia from water in the generator. Rocky Research's generator uses a special construction to achieve high-efficiency vapor separation, and absorber performance is increased by a heat-transfer surface enhancement that provides good surface wetting at part-load conditions. Efficient operation at partial loads is also achieved by using a pulsing thermal expansion valve that allows for refrigerant flow control over a wide range of capacities and temperatures. These innovations significantly reduce the cycling losses of traditional gas-fired absorption systems. The initial technology developed with these innovations was a 5-ton absorption chiller. To enable the unit to operate as a heat pump at low outdoor temperatures, Rocky Research developed a solution pump with a positive return, which allows for lower solution operating pressures and temperatures. The heat pump will operate at temperatures as low as -22°F and does not require supplemental heating from an electric resistance heater until approximately 0°F. This capability will allow the Rocky Research heat pump to be used in most of the U.S. without any supplemental heating.

Rocky Research's 5-ton Absorption Chiller/Heat Pump.

Applications

Can be used as an alternative to vapor-compression air conditioners and heat pumps in residential and light commercial applications.

Capabilities

- Offers variable-capacity operation and reduces cycling losses by using a high-turndown gas burner and a pulsing thermal expansion valve for refrigerant flow control.
- Achieves a cooling coefficient of performance (COP) of 0.7 at an ambient temperature of 95°F and a part-load COP of more than 0.8 at 85°F.
- Achieves a heating COP of 1.4 at 47°F and can provide heat pumping down to -22°F (with supplemental resistance heating beginning at 0°F).

Benefits

Safety

Reduces the chances of brownouts and blackouts during summer heat waves when stress on the electrical grid from air conditioning loads is exceptionally high.

Versatility

Can use natural gas, propane, captured solar heat, and exhaust heat from engines and turbines to power the generator.

Contact Information:
Uwe Rockenfeller
Email: uwe.rockenfeller@rockyresearch.com
Phone: (702) 293-0851
Rocky Research
P.O. Box 61800
Boulder City, NV 89006-1800
Website: http://www.rockyresearch.com

Comboflair®: An Integrated HVAC and Water Heating System

Packaged System Provides Energy-Efficient Space Conditioning for Manufactured Homes

Manufactured housing is an important part of the U.S. residential market because it constitutes a major portion of affordable housing for low-to-moderate income American families. According to the U.S. Census Bureau, the average cost of a manufactured home in 2009 was $41.24/ft^2, whereas site-built homes averaged $83.89/ft^2 (excluding land). While the structural quality of manufactured homes has been improving, few improvements have been made to the energy-related comfort or the efficiency of HVAC systems in these homes. The need for improved space conditioning systems has been identified by the manufactured housing industry and the U.S. Department of Energy's (DOE's) Building America Program.

With assistance from DOE's Building Technologies Program, DeLima Associates and a team of project partners have developed the Comboflair, a space conditioning system that enhances energy-related comfort and reduces energy consumption in manufactured homes. The Comboflair combines a packaged air conditioning system with a small-duct, high-velocity air distribution system. A natural gas or propane water heater supplies both the hot water and space heating needs of the home, with space heating delivered via a hydronic coil in the air handler. This arrangement is more cost-effective than separate water heating and electric resistance space heating.

Electric resistance heating is the most common heating technology offered with manufactured homes due to its low first cost. Unfortunately, such systems suffer from high operating costs. In the South, where most manufactured homes are sold, the 2009 average residential price of electricity ($29/MMBtu) was more than double that of natural gas ($14/MMBtu). The Comboflair reduces heating costs by using natural gas instead of electricity and also eliminates the quality control problems associated with conventional on-site installation of air conditioners by local HVAC subcontractors. The self-contained packaged unit can be tested and installed at the manufactured home factory prior to shipping.

Technology History

- Developed by DeLima Associates, with assistance from a team of project partners from the HVAC, manufactured home, and propane/natural gas industries.

- Currently focused on bringing the completed technology to the market.

DeLima Associates' 4-ton Comboflair Unit.

Applications

Can be used to improve HVAC energy efficiency and indoor air quality in manufactured homes.

Capabilities
- Provides 2-4 tons of cooling via a vapor-compression system and uses either gas hydronic heating or an electric heat pump with gas hydronic auxiliary heating.
- Achieves a cooling seasonal energy efficiency ratio (SEER) of 13.
- Provides sufficient hot water to maintain a shower temperature of 105°F for more than 20 minutes while maintaining an indoor temperature of 70°F during a peak winter day in the southern U.S.
- Maintains indoor relative humidity between 25-35%.

Benefits

Ease of Installation

Installs as a single packaged unit at the manufactured home facility. Offers a small footprint (30" x 42" 4-ton unit) for minimal space consumption.

Energy Savings

Uses a small-duct, high-velocity air distribution system to minimize the loss of conditioned air via duct leakage.

> Contact Information:
> Henry DeLima
> *Email:* HDL630@aol.com
> *Phone:* (703) 448-9653
> DeLima Associates
> 1227 Providence Terrace, Suite L-2
> McLean, VA 22101
> Website: http://www.delimaassociates.com

Energy-Efficient Façades for Green Buildings

Solar Heat and Power System Generates and Conserves Energy for Building Utility Loads

Solar energy systems on building façades can provide multiple benefits from both energy conservation and occupant quality perspectives. A high-quality system should reduce the heat and glare of direct sunlight while allowing diffuse natural daylight to flood the interior of a building. The façade should maximize the amount of solar energy captured for conversion or storage so that electricity and heat can be optimally redistributed among a building's multiple utility systems to conserve energy. If possible, the design should also be aesthetically attractive for architectural markets.

An integrated, concentrating (IC) solar façade that meets all of these requirements has been developed by the Rensselaer Polytechnic Institute (RPI) Center for Architecture Science and Ecology, with assistance from the U.S. Department of Energy's Building Technologies Program, the New York State Energy Research and Development Authority, and the New York State Foundation for Science, Technology and Innovation. The system is architecturally integrated into the façades and roof atria of buildings while still providing outside views and diffuse daylight for the building's occupants. These benefits are accomplished by miniaturizing and distributing the essential components of concentrating photovoltaic (PV) technology within the weather-sealed windows of building envelopes. The IC system produces electricity with PV cells and captures the remaining solar energy via coolant flow through the receiver on which the cells are mounted. This coolant can be directed through heat exchangers to provide thermal energy for hot water or space heating applications. Sun-tracking technology is used to adjust the angle of the PV cells throughout the day. Direct sunlight perpendicular to the façade surface is used for electricity generation, while diffuse incident sunlight enters the building to provide the benefits of natural daylighting.

The IC solar façade system has been demonstrated in several "proof of concept" lab and building-scale prototypes, whose performance is currently being monitored. The first large-scale demonstration will be a retrofit and addition to a New York City midtown atrium, where a 25-ft-high and 260-ft-long daylighting system will be installed in the south-facing façade.

Prototype Installation of RPI's Energy-EfficientFaçade at the Syracuse Center of Excellence.

Technology History
- Developed by the Rensselaer Polytechnic Institute Center for Architecture Science and Ecology.
- Licensed by HeliOptix, LLC.
- Preparing for large-scale deployment on commercial buildings.

Applications
Can be integrated into façades, clerestories, roofs, and atria of commercial buildings to provide electrical power, thermal energy, enhanced daylighting, and reduced solar gain.

Capabilities
- Produces electricity (peak >2.72 kW/m^2) and hot water (peak >3.93 kW/m^2).
- Provides diffuse daylighting at 3.2 klux.
- Reduces heat gain and glare from direct sunlight.

Benefits

Cost Savings

Reduces building cooling and lighting equipment requirements and operating costs.

Ease of Integration

Modular design easily attaches to a variety of existing building structures or can be implemented during new construction.

Emissions Reductions

Reduces emissions from fossil fuel consumption by using renewable solar energy to meet building electrical and thermal loads.

Contact Information:
Anna Dyson
Email: dysona@rpi.edu
Phone: (212) 618-3962
Rensselaer Polytechnic Institute - CASE
14 Wall Street 24th Floor
New York, NY 10005
Website: http://www.case.rpi.edu

Foundation Heat Pump

Ground Source Heat Pump Provides
Low-Cost Building Heating, Cooling and Hot Water

Improving commercial and residential building energy efficiency will contribute greatly to achieving the U.S. Department of Energy's (DOE's) 2020 50% cost-effective energy savings target. Achieving this goal will require cost-effective, energy-efficient technologies as well as public awareness and attitude and behavior modification. High-efficiency geothermal or ground source heat pumps (GSHPs) are ideal for use in HVAC systems and for hot water heating. Widespread adoption has been limited by the high cost of excavation and drilling to install the in-ground components. The size of the in-ground installation is directly related to the building's heating and cooling loads. In a high-performance building, these loads are minimized and the foundation excavation cost reduced.

With assistance from DOE's Building Technologies Program, Oak Ridge National Laboratory (ORNL) has developed and demonstrated a foundation heat exchanger. Heat flow occurs between the foundation and the surrounding soil containing the heat exchanger piping, which transfers some useful energy to the GSHPs. The system reduces electricity use and peak demand, and the installation costs were reduced because the system uses the foundation and existing utility trenches excavated for the building's construction.

ORNL has installed GSHP technologies in several residential installations, along with other energy-efficient technologies. ORNL is currently working with private industry partners to accelerate the application of GSHP technologies.

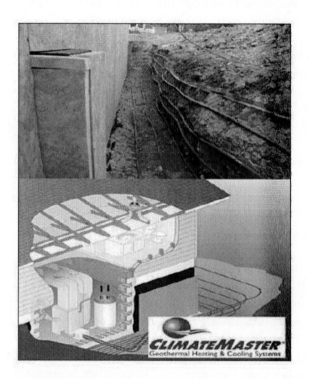

ORNL's Residential Ground Source Heat Pump System.

Technology History
- Developed by ORNL and industry partners.
- Working with industry partners to bring the technology to market.

Applications

Can be used in residential and small commercial building applications.

Capabilities
- Provides the same amenities as conventional air source heat pump systems but with lower peak space heating loads.
- Recovers "free" ground source heat for building utility use.

Benefits

Cost Savings

Reduces electricity consumption and peak demand.

Integration

Uses existing excavated foundation and utility trenches to reduce installation cost.

```
Contact Information:
Jeffrey Christian
Email: christianje@ornl.gov
Phone: (856) 574-5207
Oak Ridge National Laboratory
P.O. Box 2008, MS-6070
Oak Ridge, TN 37831-6070
Website: http://www.ornl.gov
```

HyPak: A High-Efficiency Rooftop Packaged HVAC System

New Technology Provides Low-Cost,
Energy-Efficient Space Conditioning

More than half of U.S. commercial building space is cooled by packaged HVAC equipment, most of which are rooftop units (RTUs). RTUs are popular because they are inexpensive, provide zonal control, are easy to install, can be serviced without disrupting building occupants, and are familiar to the HVAC industry. Unfortunately, existing RTUs are also very inefficient. Conventional RTUs often have single-speed motors for their supply and exhaust blowers, which consume the same amount of power regardless of changes in airflow requirements. In addition, the air-cooled condensers found in many RTUs struggle to reject heat at high outdoor temperatures, which increases the workload of the unit's compressor. An improved RTU design is needed that offers the advantages of conventional RTUs and energy-efficient operation.

With assistance from the U.S. Department of Energy's Building Technologies Program, Davis Energy Group, Inc. (DEG), is developing the HyPak, an RTU that combines several innovative features to reduce HVAC energy consumption. The design uses a novel cooling tower (known as the "counterflow evaporative water cooler" or CEWC) to cool condenser water and simultaneously pre-cool outdoor ventilation air. Evaporative cooling allows the condenser to operate near the ambient wet-bulb temperature instead of dry-bulb, which significantly improves performance in hot, dry conditions. The HyPak uses an oversized evaporator coil relative to conventional RTUs, which allows for a higher evaporative temperature and therefore reduces the power consumption of the compressor. A wide fin spacing (8 fins per inch versus 15 in a conventional RTU) is used on the evaporator coil to minimize pressure drop and reduce the chance of bacterial growth across the fins.

Additional energy-saving features of the HyPak include variable-speed blowers to maximize efficiency in partial-load conditions and a variable-capacity tankless gas water heater (coupled to a hydronic air coil) for heating. DEG plans to develop a unit that can deliver up to 100% outdoor air (for nights when the outdoor air temperature is less than that of the return air) and an automated process to reduce the cost of assembling the CEWC.

Prototype Installation of DEG's HyPak Rooftop HVAC System .

Technology History

- Developed by DEG, in partnership with Munters Corporation and with support from the National Energy Technology Laboratory.
- Planning to develop a unit that can deliver up to 100% outdoor air and an automated process for assembly of the unit's CEWC.

Applications

Can be used to provide energy-efficient space conditioning in commercial buildings.

Capabilities

- Provides 10-30 tons of cooling capacity with an energy efficiency ratio of 16-20, depending on outdoor conditions.
- Cools condenser inlet water to 75°F and pre-cools outdoor air from 105°F to 80°F at a wet-bulb temperature of 70°F.
- Delivers up to 40% ventilation air using variable-speed supply and exhaust blowers to match airflow requirements.

Benefits

Cost Savings

Reduces peak HVAC electricity consumption by using evaporative cooling, which is most effective at high outdoor temperatures.

Indoor Air Quality

Improves indoor air quality by using a high-efficiency air filter and ultraviolet light disinfection system, which prevents any biological contaminants in the supply air stream from entering the building.

```
Contact Information:
Mark Berman
Email: mjberm@davisenergy.com
Phone: (530) 753-1100, ext. 14
Davis Energy Group, Inc.
123 C Street Davis, CA 95616
Website: http://www.davisenergy.com/
```

Improving Electric Motor Efficiency

Testing and Simulation Process Evaluates
Motor Materials, Design, and Performance

Electric motors in the commercial and residential sectors account for roughly 65% of U.S. electricity consumption, or about 2.5 billion MWh. Improvements in electric motor efficiency can therefore contribute significantly to the U.S. Department of Energy's (DOE's) 2015 energy conservation goals. Motor efficiency can be improved by characterizing and understanding the magnetic properties of the materials used in motor components. A comprehensive testing method is needed to characterize losses during motor operation and to evaluate the effects of material lamination thickness, annealing, and processing.

With assistance from DOE's Building Technologies Program, SMMA - The Motor and Motion Association, and a consortium of industry partners are developing test methods, equipment, and software simulation models to improve the efficiency of electric motors used in commercial and residential applications. The project is investigating current design conventions, materials, and manufacturing processes. SMMA's testing methods examine a greater number of motor operating parameters across a wider range of conditions than current procedures, and do so in a reduced amount of time. The expanded test parameter dataset reduces errors arising from extrapolation of motor behavior to conditions not included in conventional tests. A computer-controlled system is being developed that will facilitate flexible, customizable, multi-parameter testing (including Epstein, Toroid, and Single Strip tests) in accordance with the ASTM A343 industry standard.

Data from the new testing method were used to improve the validity and accuracy of existing electric motor simulation models. The simulation results have been compared with conventional design results, allowing the differences to be analyzed for potential motor efficiency gains. An enhanced computer modeling motor design package was also developed and tested by an industry partner. This computer aided design (CAD) package was used in the assembly of a new motor prototype, resulting in improved efficiency and performance behavior that matched predictions by the computer simulation. Further evaluation and research will be performed with the goal of building upon the demonstrated improvements.

SMMA's Motor Characterization Test Bed and CAD Output.

Technology History
- Developed by SMMA, with assistance from Clarkson University, the Electric Motor Education and Research Foundation, and industry partners.
- Seeking research funding opportunities to develop materials and components for improving motor efficiency.

Applications
Can be used to improve electric motor efficiency in commercial and residential applications.

Capabilities
- Improves the throughput of testing and material characterization.
- Enhances product development and enables motor components to be designed for manufacturability.

Benefits

Cost Savings
Automates testing procedures and streamlines the motor design and development process.

Efficiency

Reduces electric motor losses, thereby providing performance and efficiency gains.

Productivity

Extends battery life and reduces downtime from motor failure or maintenance.

Contact Information:
Bill Chambers
Email: bill.chambers@smma.org
Phone: (508) 979-5935
SMMA – The Motor & Motion Association
PO Box P182 S. Dartmouth, MA 02748
Website: http://www.smma.org

Predictive Optimal Control of Active and Passive Building Thermal Storage Inventory

New Control Technology Reduces HVAC Energy Costs in Commercial Buildings

The cooling of commercial buildings contributes significantly to the peak demand for electricity experienced during mid-afternoon in the summer months of the year. Low electricity prices during off-peak hours (i.e., nights and early mornings) make the use of thermal energy storage (TES) technologies an attractive strategy for reducing HVAC energy costs. TES is typically employed via an active or a passive approach. Active systems use a building's cooling equipment to remove heat from an energy storage medium (e.g., ice or chilled water) and then use that medium to provide cooling during the day. Passive thermal storage involves night precooling of a building's structure and internal equipment, which serve as heat sinks during the day.

With assistance from the U.S. Department of Energy's Building Technologies Program, the University of Colorado at Boulder has developed an improved form of predictive optimal control for optimizing the use of both active and passive TES strategies in commercial buildings. The technology uses information such as short-term weather forecasts, electricity price data, and a building's energy profile (e.g., size, structural materials, envelope characteristics, and occupancy) to devise an optimal TES control strategy, which it then delivers to a building's automated HVAC controls. Testing conducted during this project showed that the combined use of active and passive TES significantly increases cost savings compared with either method used on its own.

The control technology has been demonstrated by Clean Urban Energy, Inc. (CUE), in several large commercial buildings in downtown Chicago in anticipation of the technology entering the market. CUE has also developed a scalable, online version of the control software that can be expanded to simultaneously deliver control instructions to a large number of buildings.

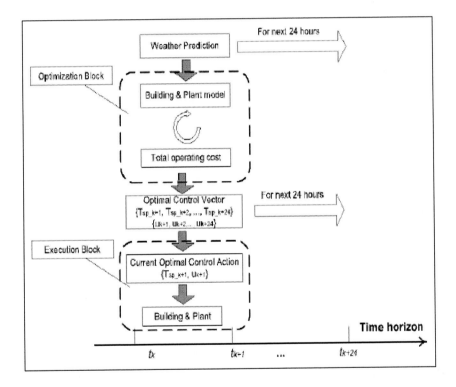

Flow Diagram for the University of Colorado's Active and Passive TES Control Technology for Commercial Buildings.

Technology History
- Developed by the University of Colorado at Boulder, in partnership with Clean Urban Energy, Inc.
- Currently being demonstrated in several large commercial buildings in the Chicago metropolitan area.

Applications

Can be used to predictively optimize thermal storage strategies in commercial buildings to shift HVAC electricity consumption from peak to non-peak hours in response to real-time pricing and demand response signals.

Capabilities

- Uses data such as short-term weather forecasts and energy prices to optimize thermal energy storage strategies for reducing HVAC power costs.
- Delivers hourly control instructions to a building's automation system.

Benefits

Cost Savings

Reduces HVAC operating costs by shifting electricity consumption from peak to off-peak (nighttime) hours.

Grid Efficiency

Increases grid efficiency by shifting consumption from peaking power plants to more efficient baseload plants.

Stability

Reduces daytime strain on the electrical grid and helps combat the problem of negative nighttime electricity prices due to an excess of generation capacity and a lack of demand.

Contact Information:
Prof. Gregor P. Henze, Ph.D., P.E.
Email: gregor.henze@colorado.edu
Phone: (303) 492-1094
Clean Urban Energy, Inc.
711 South Dearborn Street, Unit 404
Chicago, IL 60605
Website: http://www.cleanurbanenergy.com/

Thermoelectric Materials for Waste Heat Recovery

Nanoscale, Multilayer Film Deposition Process Increases Efficiency of TE Materials

The thermoelectric (TE) effect is the direct conversion of a thermal gradient (temperature difference, ΔT) into an electrical potential difference (voltage) and vice versa. The ideal application of TE technology is in buildings, where waste heat from furnaces, water heaters, and concentrated solar energy systems could be recovered. TE devices operated in reverse could potentially compete with and eventually exceed the performance of commercial vapor compression cooling systems used in refrigeration and air conditioning units. The cost, efficiency, and performance of TE devices must be improved if TE-based systems are to become alternatives to conventional building technologies. TE material efficiency is expressed as a value of ZT, the material's "figure of merit", Z, times its average absolute operating temperature, T. Historically, ZT values for TE devices have been around 1.0, which is insufficient to compete with vapor compression cooling systems. TE coolers in use today have a coefficient of performance (COP) of about 0.5, whereas most air conditioners and refrigerators have COP values of 3-5.

With assistance from the U.S. Department of Energy's Building Technologies Program, Hi-Z Technology, Inc., is developing a unique nanoscale materials approach to overcome the cost and efficiency limitations that have prevented TE systems from being deployed in large markets. This technique produces a quantum well thermoelectric (QWTE) device, which has an in-plane film topology to control heat and current flow. Alternating layers of semiconductors having different electronic properties are deposited and yield a ZT >2.0 and superior electrical performance compared with bulk alloys. The process can be automated to enable affordable, high-volume fabrication and uses readily available, abundant, nontoxic materials. Hi-Z is continuing to develop the technology, and early results have demonstrated ZT >3.0 at room temperature and ZT >6.0 at 325°C. Research is being conducted to fabricate these materials into modules, reduce heat losses within the devices, and improve the electrical contacts on the thin films. Hi-Z expects to produce the first high-efficiency device within the next two years.

Technology History
- Developed by Hi-Z Technology, Inc.
- Currently improving device technology and seeking manufacturing partnerships.

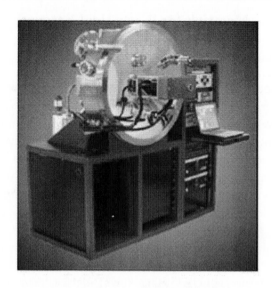

Hi-Z's Sputter Coating Systemfor Producing QWTE Devices.

Applications

Can be used to convert waste heat from furnaces, water heaters, and solar panels into electricity, or act as a heat pump for refrigeration and air conditioning if supplied with an electric current.

Capabilities

- Achieves up to 50 W output at 15% efficiency; Hi-Z's current module produces 14 W at 5% efficiency.
- Achieves a COP of 3.0, which is comparable to conventional mechanical vapor compression cooling systems.

Benefits

Cost Savings

Reduces manufacturing costs using automated process and readily available Si, C, B, and N.

Durability

Uses solid-state, high-temperaturecompatible materials that require less maintenance than conventional systems.

Environmental
Avoids using toxic and expensive materials such as Te, Co, As, Ir, and Pb.
Reduces emissions by reducing energy consumption.

Contact Information: Dan Krommenhoek *Email:* d.krommenhoek@hi-z.com *Phone:* (865) 695-6660 Hi-Z Technology, Inc. 7606 Miramar Rd., #7400 San Diego, CA 92126 Website: http://www.hi-z.com

100 Lumen/Watt Warm White LED

Improved LEDs Provide High-Efficiency Warm White Lighting
Over the last few years, rapid progress has been made in improving the performance of phosphor-converted indium gallium nitride (InGaN) white light-emitting diodes (LEDs). Efficacies of available blue-LED-pumped white phosphor products have increased to over 100 lm/W for providing 'cool' white light with a correlated color temperature (CCT) >5000 K. Warm white (CCT values of 2700-3300 K) LED performance lags behind cool white by up to 30% in efficacy and light output. Reduced efficacy has historically been a tradeoff in order to provide warm white light, which has an incandescent-like appearance desired by many consumers. Improved efficacy is needed so that warm white LEDs can replace incandescent, halogen, and compact fluorescent lamps in general illumination applications.

With assistance from the U.S. Department of Energy's Building Technologies Program, Philips Lumileds Lighting Company is developing warm white LEDs for use in commercial and residential applications. The devices will deliver illumination-grade warm white light with a CCT of 2700-3500 K, 800 lm output, an efficacy of 100 lm/W, and a color rendering index (CRI) of 90 at 350 mA drive current. The LED will contain a 2 x 2 mm InGaN die and a new phosphor material called Lumiramic®. This plate-in-die on ceramic package can be surface mounted.

A new high-power LED package is also being developed that integrates the 4 mm^2 InGaN chips, the new phosphor material, and an optical lens on a ceramic submount. Prototype devices driven at 700 mA have produced over

800 lm with an efficacy of 99 lm/W, a CRI of 75, and a CCT of 3300 K. Product commercialization is currently underway.

Warm White LED Package Developed by Philips Lumileds.

Technology History
- Developed by Philips Lumileds Lighting Company.
- Currently transitioning from prototype design to commercial product.

Applications
Can be used for general illumination purposes such as spotlighting and downlighting.

Capabilities
- Produces warm white light with an output in excess of 800 lm at an efficacy of 100 lm/W.
- Provides a CCT of 2700-3500 K with a CRI of 90 at 350 mA drive current (CRI of 75 at 700 mA).
- Offers narrow color distribution and reduces the need for color sorting.

Benefits

Cost Savings

Reduces cost per lumen and total energy consumption of general lighting applications.

Durability

Lasts for more than 50,000 hours under normal operating conditions.

> Contact Information:
> Dr. Decai Sun
> *Email:* decai.sun@philips.com
> *Phone:* (408) 964-2868
> Philips Lumileds Lighting Company
> 370 W. Trimble Road San Jose, CA 95131
> Website: http://www.philipslumileds.com/

Affordable, High-Efficiency Solid-State Downlight Luminaires with Novel Cooling

High-Efficiency LED Replacement Lamp Saves Energy and Reduces Costs for Lighting Applications

Light-emitting diode (LED) lamps are rapidly gaining acceptance in commercial and residential lighting applications. However, thermal management and high system cost remain key barriers to broad market penetration. Passive heat sinks are often unable to manage the large heat fluxes generated by the LEDs, compromising the system efficacy and lifetime. In addition, these lamps often require high LED chip counts to meet overall lumen targets, thereby increasing the initial system cost.

To overcome these limitations, GE Global Research, with support from the Department of Energy's Building Technologies Program, has developed an LED-based 1500 lumen lamp that uses revolutionary cooling technology to improve performance and reduce lighting energy costs. GE synthetic jets are very small micro-fluidic, bellows-type devices that provide high-velocity jets of air that impinge on the LED heat sink. These jets of air increase the heat transfer rate to more than ten times that of natural convection. The improved cooling enables LED operation at high drive currents without losses in efficiency or lifetime. For a given lumen output, the synthetic jets' improved thermal management reduces the necessary LED chip count by 40%, dramatically lowering the cost of the lamp. In addition to performance and cost advantages, the synthetic jet cooling reduces LED lamp size and weight.

GE and its project partner, the University of Maryland, are currently developing physics-of-failure-based models to accurately predict product reliability and any potential failure modes. This work will lead to LED lighting systems with optimized reliability to guarantee a 50,000 hour product lifetime. The current program strategy is independent of chip-level technology. Therefore, any advances in LED chip-level performance will be additive to the technologies developed in this program. The multiple benefits offered by this improved LED technology will enable these lamps to significantly penetrate the general lighting markets.

Prototype GE Synthetic Jet Cooled LED Lamp.

Technology History
- Developed by GE Global Research in partnership with GE Lighting Systems and the University of Maryland.
- Continuing work to optimize the design for manufacturing and reliability.

Applications
Can be used as a high-efficiency replacement for conventional 1500 lumen incandescent and compact fluorescent light bulbs in both residential and commercial applications.

Capabilities
- Produces 1500 lumens at a color rendering index (CRI) of 81 and a correlated color temperature (CCT) of 3100 K.
- Achieves efficacies exceeding 50 lumens per watt (LPW) for warm white light and 75 LPW for cool white light.
- Maintains high performance over its installed lifetime through optional 180, 50, and 20 degree full width half maximum beam angle control.

Benefits

Cost Savings
Reduces initial system cost by using synthetic jet cooling, which lowers the LED chip count necessary to meet lumen output targets.

Product Quality
Offers a compact design that is half the size and weight of a 600 lumen, passively cooled lamp.

Contact Information:
Mehmet Arik
Email: arik@research.ge.com
Phone: (518) 867-9970
GE Global Research
1 Research Circle Niskayuna, NY 12309
Website: http://ge.geglobalresearch.com/

Efficient LED System-in-Module for General Lighting

SSL Device Offers Adaptable Color and Light
Output Control for General Illumination
Solid-state lighting (SSL) devices for general illumination applications have the potential to dramatically reduce the amount of energy used for lighting across the U.S. commercial, residential, and industrial sectors. In order for widespread adoption of the technology to occur, SSL products that are adaptable to current applications and lighting infrastructure are needed. In the near term, products that are compatible with conventional light fixtures and wiring are likely to be the most desirable.

With assistance from the U.S. Department of Energy's Building Technologies Program, Philips Lighting and NXP Semiconductors have developed an SSL device for general illumination that has an Edison base and a lifetime of 50,000 hours. The device integrates all the necessary components and control circuitry to provide compatibility with existing conventional fixtures. Color variability and light output control are provided via a user-friendly interface with a wired or wireless communications protocol. High-quality control is achieved by utilizing photodiode and temperature sensor inputs to the software algorithms. This highly flexible user control interface allows the SSL device to be used in a multitude of applications where color consistency, color variability, or multiple light levels are required. The onboard photodiode enables compatibility with installations that employ daylight compensation, thereby increasing value and energy savings.

Initial device efficacy targets were based on availability of red, green, blue, and amber light-emitting diodes (LEDs) that, when combined in the proper proportions, would generate white light at an efficacy of 100 lm/W. The required efficacy levels were not available during the project development and therefore produced lower efficacy results (35 lm/W at CCT = 4000 K). LED efficacies have since reached the required levels (especially for the primary colors), but white LED performance has also improved. Given these recent developments, the potential applications and markets for this technology are currently being re-evaluated, and the technology will be adapted into various SSL-related components and products.

Technology History
- Developed by Philips Lighting and NXP Semiconductors.
- Being adapted into various SSL-related components and products.

Applications
Can be used for general illumination applications requiring color-controlled white or multi-colored lighting.

Capabilities
- Achieves an efficacy of 35-70 lm/W, depending on device configuration and output mode.
- Uses color and light output level control.
- Achieves full-range dimming without experiencing color shift.
- Uses addressable device communication via wire or wireless protocol.

Philips' Fully Integrated, Controllable SSL Technology.

Benefits

Adaptability
Offers adjustable color and light output that can be tailored to suit differing applications.

Durability
Operates for 50,000 hours under normal conditions.

Energy Savings
Uses device programming for daylighting and usage (occupancy) control.

Contact Information:
James Gaines
Email: jim.gaines@philips.com
Phone: (781) 418-9292
Philips Lighting
3 Burlington Woods Drive, 4th floor
Burlington, MA 01803
Website: http://www.lighting.philips.com

LECD Technology for Lighting and Signage

Durable, Electro-Ceramescent, Light-Emitting Device Operates on Low-Power Requirements

A large demand exists for a new type of artificial lighting that is highly visible in darkened conditions, energy efficient, and environmentally stable. Such a light source should also be nonglaring in response to the expanding dark-sky initiative, which strives to reduce the prevalence of light pollution around major urban areas. Developing more energy-efficient lighting sources is a growing trend; alternative technologies currently on the market meet some of these demands, but not all.

With assistance from the U.S. Department of Energy's Building Technologies Program, Meadow River Enterprises, Inc., Ecer Technologies, LLC, and their research partners are developing an electro-ceramescent lighting technology. The product is made by applying several layers of ceramics on a thin piece of steel. Encapsulated in one of these layers is a mixture of phosphors, which emit photons when electrically energized. The electron-to-photon conversion is very efficient and does not depend on heating a filament to generate light. This new light source is referred to as a light-emitting-ceramic device (LECD).

Ecer Technologies' LECD Signs.

LECD technology is very durable, with an expected lifetime of 50,000 hours. Unless a mechanical defect occurs, the LECD will not fail catastrophically but will fade slowly over time. The technology operates on either an AC or DC supply, and its low power requirement allows signs to be powered by solar panels. LECDs have improved visibility at night and during inclement weather, and do not have a "halo" effect in fog, rain, or snow. These features are excellent safety benefits for the transportation sector. LECD lighting has many potential uses including industrial, commercial and highway signage, directional markers, and residential landscaping products.

Technology History

- Developed by Meadow River Enterprises, Inc., and Ecer Technologies, LLC.
- Focusing on marketing strategies for commercialization and startup of a manufacturing plant.

Applications

Can be used in a variety of signage and lighting applications.

Capabilities

- Produces clear, nonglaring light with a power consumption of less than 0.2 W per square foot.
- Operates over a wide temperature range (-40°F to over 190°F).
- Allows signs to be powered by solar panels.

Benefits

Cost Savings

Enables increased material utilization and lower costs through use of a continuous flow manufacturing process.

Durability

Offers a life expectancy of over 50,000 hours. Produces a negligibly small amount of heat and does not de-laminate over time.

Efficiency

Requires one-tenth of the energy consumed by similar light-emitting diode applications.

Environmental
Provides nonglaring light in response to the dark-sky initiative.

Contact Information:
Don Osborne
Email: dosborne@citynet.net
Phone: (304) 497-9986
Ecer Technologies, LLC
HC71 Box 145A
Crawley, WV 24931
Website: http://www.ecertechnologies.com

Scaling up: Kilo-Lumen SSL Exceeding100 Lumens per Watt

Remote Phosphor, Thermal Management,
and Driver Technologies Provide High Efficacy SSL

Currently, very few reasonably priced, high-performance solid state A19 lamps can replace existing 60-watt incandescent lamps with an output of 900 lumens, a color rendering index (CRI) above 90, and uniform "spherical" output. The traditional approach of phosphor-coated, blue light-emitting diodes (LEDs) results in reduced system efficiency due to light being reflected back into the LED, where it heats up the chip and the phosphor. This phenomenon, known as Stokes Shift Loss, reduces the lumen output and lifetime of LEDs. A new packaging design is needed that will improve the thermal management and efficacy of A19 LED lamps.

With assistance from the U.S. Department of Energy's (DOE's) Building Technologies Program, Light Prescriptions Innovators (LPI), LLC, and their technology partners are developing technologies that will address the efficiency issues associated with conventional phosphor-coated LEDs. LPI's design places the phosphor at a distance from the LED itself and uses advanced focusing lenses to direct blue light from the LED chip(s) to the phosphor. White light from the excited phosphor is prevented from returning to its source by special optics, which increases efficacy and prevents the LED chip(s) from overheating. The design also protects the phosphor itself from heat given off by blue light production in the LEDs. A cooler phosphor temperature improves light output uniformity and quality over a wide variety of operating conditions. To improve the lamp's thermal management, LPI has developed a passive cooling method that creates an air vortex that works in either vertical or horizontal lamp orientations. LPI has also developed a new LED electronic driver technology that reduces the size and loads of several key components (capacitors), positively impacting the reliability of the driver. These new technologies will extend the lifetime of the prototype lamps that are currently under development.

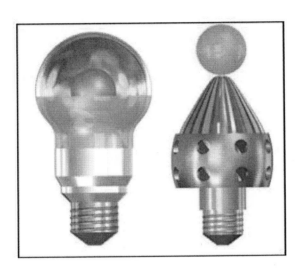

LPI's Remote Phosphor in an A19 LED Lamp.

Technology History
- Developed by LPI, with assistance from Osram Opto Semiconductors.
- Planning to submit design into DOE's L-Prize competition in first quarter 2011.

Applications
Can be used as an energy-efficient alternative to incandescent and compact fluorescent lighting, especially for applications that require high-quality color rendering and lamp durability.

Capabilities
- Achieves an efficacy >90 lm/W.
- Adjusts device output automatically to prevent overheating.
- Achieves a CRI >90 in a color temperature range of 2700-3100 K.
- Dims down to 20% of maximum output.

Benefits

Durability
Achieves 25,000 hours of operating lifetime.

Manufacturability
Provides compatibility with high-volume manufacturing processes.

Product Quality
Improves the quality and efficacy of light using patented phosphor, thermal management, and dimming technologies.

Contact Information:
Waqidi Falicoff
Email: wfalicoff@lpi-llc.us
Phone: (714) 553-6490
Light Prescriptions Innovators, LLC
2400 Lincoln Ave Altadena, CA 91001
Website: http://www.lpi-llc.com

Bulk GaN Substrate Growth Technique

Novel Process Enables Production of High-Quality Solid-State Devices

Gallium nitride (GaN)-based semiconductor devices are gaining wider market acceptance in solid-state lighting, laser diode, and power electronics applications. The final performance characteristics of these devices are heavily influenced by the quality of the substrate on which the devices are grown. Conventional wafer epitaxy is constrained by the crystalline quality of the substrate material, which is typically silicon carbide, sapphire, or silicon. This heteroepitaxial growth method often results in an increased defect density in the final product wafer due to slight mismatches in the crystal lattices and thermal expansion properties of the substrate and the wafer. These defects in turn lead to poor electrical and thermal performance in the resulting solid-state devices. The quality of the devices can be improved via homoepitaxial growth, whereby GaN-based devices are grown on GaN substrates. Large quantities of high-quality GaN crystal substrate are therefore needed.

With assistance from the U.S. Department of Energy's Building Technologies Program and Office of Electricity, Sandia National Laboratories (SNL) is developing a new crystal growth technology, called Electrochemical Solution Growth (ESG), to produce bulk GaN substrates for fabricating thin film optoelectronic devices. The ESG process is cost-effective and can be scaled to meet industry-desired diameters for the product GaN boules (and the resulting substrate wafers). Bulk GaN crystal growth is currently limited by the difficulties in producing adequate conditions for a reaction between nitrogen and gallium. The ESG method addresses this challenge by producing a reactive form of nitrogen at atmospheric pressure in a solution. The process builds on well-developed concepts from rotating disk reactor metal-organic chemical vapor deposition (MOCVD) technology. Using a rotating crystal seed surface, ions diffuse across a fluid boundary layer near the surface and deposit on the surface to form a single-crystal GaN boule. The technique produces high-quality material (10^2 dislocations/cm^2), resulting in improved performance and durability for GaN-based devices grown from the substrates.

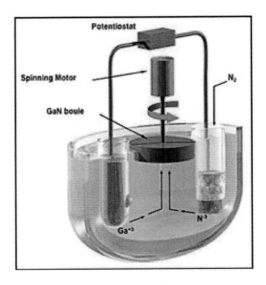

SNL's ESG Process for Producing Bulk GaN Substrates.

Technology History
- Developed by SNL.
- Continuing R&D involves optimization of the experimental conditions for GaN crystal formation.

Applications
Can be used to grow improved crystalline GaN substrates for subsequent epitaxial manufacturing of high-quality solid-state optoelectronic devices.

Capabilities
- Produces high-quality bulk GaN containing only 10^2 dislocations/cm^2.
- Enables improved solid-state device performance and durability.

Benefits

Reliability
Uses proven concepts from existing crystal growth applications, such as rotating disk reactor MOCVD technology.

Scalability
Enables the GaN boules to reach industry-desired diameters for the resulting substrate wafers.

Versatility
Can be applied to produce many different types of solid-state devices across multiple markets.

Contact Information:
Dr. Karen Waldrip
Email: knwaldr@sandia.gov
Phone: (505) 844-1619
Sandia National Laboratories
PO Box 5800 Albuquerque, NM 87185
Website: http://www.sandia.gov/

Enhancing Quantum Efficiency of InGaN-Based LEDs

Staggered Growth of InGaN Quantum Wells Improves Quantum Efficiency of Nitride LEDs
Concerns over the rising cost of oil and the environmental impact of carbon emissions have prompted a national discussion about energy conservation and renewable sources of energy. Solid-state lighting (SSL) could significantly reduce the amount of energy consumed to produce light for residential, commercial, and industrial applications. High-performance visible-

light emitters are crucial for widespread adoption of SSL. Conventional III-Nitride light-emitting-diode (LED) devices must overcome major challenges to achieve the high performance required for SSL. Polarization fields within indium gallium nitride (InGaN) quantum wells (QWs) lead to charge separation, which in turn reduces the radiative efficiency and internal quantum efficiency of nitride LEDs (green and blue).

With assistance from the U.S. Department of Energy's Building Technologies Program, Lehigh University is developing staggered InGaN QWs to address charge separation constraints in nitride LEDs. Staggered InGaN QWs combined with high and low indium composition InGaN layers improves the radiative recombination rate in the QW active region, resulting in increased radiative and internal quantum efficiency. The prototype nitride LEDs were produced by a newly developed process that used a graded growth temperature profiling technique and metal organic chemical vapor deposition (MOCVD). The process has potential for development in commercial applications.

Prototype nitride LEDs, whose nanostructure was first optimized by computer simulation, were fabricated and achieved three times the output power and efficiency compared with a conventional device. Lehigh is currently applying for patents on these optimized nanostructures and the MOCVD fabrication process. New funding opportunities and partnerships are being investigated to apply the process commercially.

Lehigh's MOCVD Process and InGaN LEDs.

Technology History
- Developed by Lehigh University.
- Applying for patents and seeking funding and commercial partnership opportunities.

Applications
Can be used to improve the internal quantum efficiency of InGaN-based LEDs.

Capabilities
- Reduces charge separation effects.
- Increases output power and efficiency of InGaN LEDs by two to three times.
- Uses standard MOCVD equipment for device fabrication and can be easily commercialized.
- Uses computer simulation of device nanostructure to optimize device design and improve performance.

Benefits

Cost Savings
Reduces the cost of final LED products by increasing the production yield and efficiency of InGaN LEDs.

Durability
Enhances device structure, which decreases lattice defects and increases device lifetime.

Efficiency
Enables higher efficiency LEDs for SSL.

Contact Information:
Dr. Nelson Tansu
Email: tansu@lehigh.edu
Phone: (610) 758-2678
Lehigh University – Packard Laboratory
19 Memorial Drive West Bethlehem, PA 18105
Website: http://www.ece.lehigh.edu

Growth Technique for Large-Diameter AlN Single Crystal

Epitaxial Process Improves Lattice-Matched Substrates Used for Manufacturing LEDs

Superior energy savings potential, longer lifetime, and higher efficacy make nitride-based light-emitting diodes (LEDs) the key devices to replace incandescent and fluorescent lighting. A primary issue preventing higher efficacies in LEDs is poor crystalline quality of their nitride epitaxial layers (epilayers). Lattice mismatching and differences in the substrate crystal structure often lead to defects in the LED devices. High-quality nitride epilayers can be grown on aluminum nitride (AlN) substrates and enable high brightness LEDs to be fabricated. The increased efficacy of these LEDs would be sufficient for general lighting applications.

With the assistance of a U.S. Department of Energy Small Business Innovation Research grant, Fairfield Crystal Technology, LLC, is developing a process for AlN substrate growth that will enable fabrication of highly efficient LEDs for solid-state lighting. The reproducibility of the process has been demonstrated for AlN growth for multi-grain AlN crystal boules up to 2 inches in diameter and up to 25 mm in length. A specially designed crucible successfully produced standalone AlN single-crystal boules up to 9 mm in diameter. Polished AlN crystal wafers have also been used to fabricate epiready AlN single crystal samples for group III-nitride epitaxy.

In addition to LEDs, the high-quality AlN substrates can be used to fabricate other types of nitride-based devices, such as blue laser diodes for optical recording, high-frequency devices for telecommunications, and ultraviolet detectors for analytical and homeland security applications. Other possible applications for the devices produced by this technology include medical, dental, and industrial imaging.

Technology History
- Developed by Fairfield Crystal Technology, LLC.
- Currently demonstrating the technology to solid-state device manufacturers for potential applications, licensing, and partnership.

Applications
Can be used to fabricate AlN substrates for manufacturing LEDs and other solid-state devices.

Fairfield's AlN Fabrication System, AlN Crystal, and Substrates.

Capabilities

- Produces AlN crystal boules of up to 2 inches in diameter and 25 mm in length.
- Enables production of high-performance LEDs for solid-state lighting applications.

Benefits

Durability

Extends product lifetime, which results in a lower cost of ownership for device endusers.

Product Quality

Produces substrates with fewer defects, resulting in a reduced number of scrap devices and improved device performance.

Contact Information:
Andrew Timmerman
Email: atimmerman@fairfieldcrystal.com
Phone: (860) 354-2111 x200
Fairfield Crystal Technology, LLC
8 South End Plaza New Milford, CT 06776
Website: http://www.fairfieldcrystal.com

High-Efficiency, Nanocomposite White Light Phosphors

New Phosphors Provide High-Quality
Color Rendering and Tunable Color Temperature

Solid-state lighting (SSL) technology has long held tremendous potential as a means to improve energy efficiency and reduce waste with long-lasting, high-efficiency light fixtures. Widespread use of SSL in businesses and homes could significantly reduce overall electricity consumption in the United States. However, adoption of SSL has been slow due to the high upfront cost of replacing existing lights and the poor color rendering provided by many early SSL products. Currently available SSL lights often emit a 'cool', blue-yellow light with a correlated color temperature (CCT) of ≥ 5000 K, which many consumers are not partial to. For household lighting, most consumers are accustomed to incandescent light, which has a 'warm' CCT of around 2700 K. Current SSL solutions for providing consumer-satisfactory white light, such as discrete RGB (red-green-blue) LEDs and doped yttrium aluminum garnet (YAG) phosphors, are costly and inefficient.

With the assistance of a U.S. Department of Energy Small Business Innovation Research grant, Nanosys, Inc., is developing remote phosphor components based on proprietary quantum dot technology that address the cost, efficiency, and color quality issues of traditional LED phosphor systems. This solution enables the energy savings of the best high-efficiency SSL to be attained in applications where a CCT of 2700 K and a high color rendering index (CRI) are critical, such as the residential and hospitality markets. In addition, Nanosys' remote phosphor components are designed to be process-ready devices that can be incorporated into existing luminaire manufacturing processes and thereby reduce the cost of retooling and scale-up.

Technology History
- Developed by Nanosys, Inc.
- Continuing to improve the internal quantum efficiency and reliability of remote phosphors in preparation for manufacturing scale-up.

Applications
Can be used in lighting applications where high-quality color rendering across a range of color temperatures is desired.

Capabilities
- Produces custom white light with an efficiency ≥ 80 lm/W.

- Achieves a CRI ≥92 with a customizable CCT in the range of 2700-6500 K.
- Provides light output independent of input blue wavelength variation.

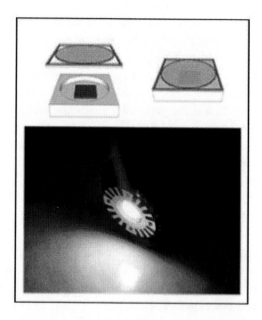

Nanosys' Remote Phosphor Affixed to Blue LED (top)and Emitting Warm White Light (bottom).

Benefits

Cost Savings

Reduces production costs by providing a process-engineered component that integrates easily into existing manufacturing processes.

Durability

Provides color stability throughout the product lifetime.

Versatility

Allows manufacturers to pursue differentiation in spectrum branding to serve markets and applications around the world with differing CCT preferences.

Contact Information:
Bob Busse
Email: bbusse@nanosysinc.com
Phone: (650) 331-2120
Nanosys, Inc.
2625 Hanover Street Palo Alto, CA 94304
Website: http://www.nanosysinc.com

High-Efficiency Nitride-Based Solid-State Lighting

Nonpolar Gallium Nitride Substrates Enable
Superior Solid-State Lighting

Lighting accounts for 20% of U.S. electricity usage and 8% of total energy usage. Conventional incandescent lamps, which currently are used in the majority of residential and commercial lighting applications, are very inefficient. Fluorescent lamps, including compact versions, are more efficient but contain toxic mercury and must be disposed of carefully. Solid-state lamps based on gallium nitride (GaN) light-emitting diodes (LEDs) are much more efficient than the best tungsten halogen incandescent lamps and already have efficiencies comparable to fluorescent lamps. In addition, solid-state lamps do not contain the toxic mercury present in fluorescent lighting products.

The use of nonpolar bulk GaN substrates for fabricating LEDs provides several key advantages for the resulting lighting products. The low-defect-density substrates ensure that most of the current injected into an LED contributes to light output, which increases the lamp's lifetime. The nonpolar orientation further improves the radiative efficiency and eliminates the wavelength shift that accompanies increasing current in conventional polar GaN LEDs. In addition, the nonpolar orientation maintains high efficiency at high current density, thereby reducing the "efficiency droop" seen in polar LEDs.

With assistance from the U.S. Department of Energy's Building Technologies Program, the University of California, Santa Barbara (UCSB), conducted research focused on epitaxial growth of nonpolar templates, along with the subsequent growth and fabrication of LEDs. The experimental results confirmed theoretical predictions and spurred the efforts towards the future commercialization of bulk nonpolar GaN substrates. Additional work has focused on light extraction methods. Coupled with nonpolar substrates, this work has significantly improved LED light output and efficiency. Continuing improvements to both internal and external efficiency will soon enable cost-effective replacement of all incandescent and most fluorescent lighting. Future commercialization of the nonpolar-GaN-based LEDs will be performed by industrial members of the UCSB Solid State Lighting and Energy Center.

UCSB's High Efficiency Nonpolar LED for Solid-State Lighting.

Technology History
- Developed by UCSB, with contributions from the Rensselaer Polytechnic Institute.
- Continuing R&D is achieving white lighting efficiencies superior to tungsten halogen lamps and comparable to fluorescent lamps.

Applications
Can be used in a variety of commercial and residential illumination applications, including automotive and specialty lighting.

Capabilities
- Achieves external quantum efficiency of >30% at 300 mA.
- Reduces wavelength shift below 2 nm from 50-300 mA.
- Increases high-power lifetime of LEDs to >5 years.

Benefits

Durability
Reduces replacement frequency and cost by using all-solid-state construction.

Energy Savings
Reduces air conditioning loads through high-efficiency operation with minimal heat generation.

Environmental
Uses non-toxic material in manufacturing, without the mercury present in fluorescent lamps.

Contact Information:
Shuji Nakamura
Email: shuji@engineering.ucsb.edu
Phone: (805) 893-5552
University of California, Santa Barbara
Materials Department Santa Barbara, CA 93106-5050
Website: http://www.materials.ucsb.edu/index.php

High-Efficiency, Non-Polar, GaN-Based LEDs

Low-Defect, Custom-Oriented GaN Substrates Produce Brighter LEDs
The quality of light-emitting diodes (LEDs) for solid-state lighting depends heavily on the device fabrication step, in which thin gallium nitride (GaN) semiconductor layers are deposited on a crystalline substrate material. Traditionally, GaN devices have been grown on foreign substrates such as sapphire or silicon carbide. Crystal lattice mismatches between the two materials cause the resulting solid-state devices to have high defect densities. These defects have a negative impact on device durability and key performance properties such as thermal conductivity. The growth of GaN devices on 'native' GaN substrates minimizes defect formation, but GaN substrate prices must fall significantly from their current level ($2000-$4000 per 2-inch diameter wafer) in order for widespread adoption to occur.

With assistance from the U.S. Department of Energy's Building Technologies Program, Inlustra Technologies, Inc., is developing scalable, cost-effective processes for manufacturing GaN substrates from which high-performance GaN devices can be fabricated. In addition to the advantages offered by native substrate growth, Inlustra's substrates enable LED performance enhancements by manipulation of a device's structure in relation to its atomic lattice structure. As opposed to traditional GaN devices, which are cut in the polar *c*-plane, Inlustra's GaN materials are oriented in the nonpolar *a*- and *m*-planes (see figure below). In this manner, a high electrical-to-optical efficiency can be obtained at elevated drive currents, thereby yielding more light output per LED chip.

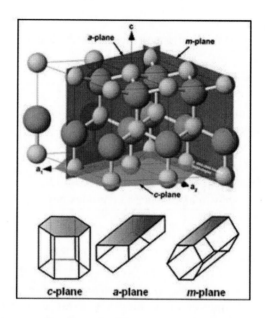

GaN Crystal Structure and c-, a-, and m-Planes.

Technology History
- Developed by Inlustra Technologies, Inc.
- Currently developing low-cost, high-volume manufacturing techniques and increasing substrate wafer diameter.

Applications
Can be used for fabricating low-defect GaN-based LEDs and laser devices.

Capabilities
- Enables stable LED light output with no color shifting at elevated drive currents.
- Improves photon conversion efficiency at high drive currents (reduces LED droop).
- Maximizes device optical performance by optimizing GaN crystal plane orientation.

Benefits

Cost Savings
Reduces the cost of producing GaNbased devices by shortening device layer deposition time and enabling simplified fabrication schemes.

Energy Savings
Increases LED efficiency, thereby achieving an equivalent lumen output with reduced electricity consumption.

Performance
Reduces internal defects and increases the high-current performance and durability of LEDs.

Contact Information:
Dr. Paul Fini
Email: fini@inlustra.com
Phone: (805) 504-4639
Inlustra Technologies, Inc.
5385 Hollister Ave., Suite #113 Santa Barbara, CA 93111
Website: http://www.inlustra.com/

High-Performance Green LEDs

Direct-Emitting Green LEDs Increase Energy
Efficiency of Solid-State Lighting Devices
Traditional incandescent lighting is highly inefficient in using electricity. Light-emitting diodes (LEDs) based on aluminum gallium indium nitrides (AlGaInN) are now at the cusp of revolutionizing the worldwide lighting market by providing significantly higher reliability and energy efficiency. However, current approaches use a combination of a single, narrow-band, blue LED and a broader yellow-emitting phosphor material that receives its excitation from the same blue LED. The result is a somewhat fractured spectrum that many consumers perceive as a harsh bluish white. This existing technology also suffers from a particularly poor color rendering in the red and green parts of the spectrum.

Rensselaer Polytechnic Institute (RPI), with assistance from the U.S. Department of Energy's Building Technologies Program, is developing novel

AlGaInN LED dies that improve performance in the green spectral region. RPI's approach uses the advantage of higher efficiency by direct emission of the desired wavelengths, bypassing the optical transformation step inside the phosphor materials. This particular implementation aims at the green spectral region which, in combination with red and blue emitters, forms a highly pleasing white that can be even further enhanced with additional colors in between. By using homoepitaxial growth on high quality bulk gallium nitride (GaN), RPI substantially enhances the green light generation efficiency and directly controls the material-inherent piezoelectric polarization. By rotating the crystal growth plane, scientists can also achieve a color-stable green emission independent of the operating current.

Expanding on these approaches offers the potential to overcome the well-known performance drop at high injection currents and to progressively deliver LED light sources at any desired wavelength throughout the visible spectrum, possibly even into the deep green and yellow colors. RPI has developed advanced prototypes and will be evaluating a demonstration unit of this technology.

Technology History
- Developed by RPI in partnership with Kyma Technologies, Inc.
- Continuing work to develop advanced prototypes and evaluate a demonstration unit.

Applications
Can be used in all solid-state lighting devices as a more energy-efficient substitute for incandescent light bulbs and fluorescent lighting.

RPI's High-Efficiency Green LED.

Capabilities
- Increases light output per LED die.
- Enables optimized color mixing and easier cooling in solid-state lighting devices.

Benefits

Cost Savings
Reduces costs by using large-scale bulk GaN substrates.

Durability
Eliminates phosphor aging issues and maintains a constant wavelength that is independent of operating current for stabilized emission color.

Energy Savings
Increases energy efficiency by directly emitting desired wavelengths, which eliminates phosphor-excitation losses associated with conventional LED technology.

Contact Information:
Christian Wetzel
Email: wetzel@rpi.edu
Phone: (518) 276-3755
Rensselaer Polytechnic Institute
110 Eighth St. Troy, NY 12180
Website: http://www.rpi.edu/~wetzel/

High-Performance Structured OLEDs and LEDs

New Fabrication Process Improves
Performance of OLED and LED Devices
Traditional organic light-emitting diode (OLED) devices use unstructured, multilayer films that present light extraction, charge injection, and reliability difficulties. On the other hand, the performance of light-emitting diode (LED) devices is sensitive to lattice defects and stresses, which are known to contribute to high resistance and structural instability. Low efficacy and unstable materials are preventing OLEDs from being widely adopted and deployed. Adoption of LEDs is hindered by defective wide bandgap

semiconductor layers, which keep LED efficacy much lower than its theoretical limit. Using structured OLEDs and LEDs would alleviate these difficulties and improve device efficacy and reliability.

With assistance from the U.S. Department of Energy's Building Technologies Program, Lawrence Berkeley National Laboratory (LBNL) is developing micro- and nano-structuring processes for fabricating OLEDs and LEDs. This structured approach to OLED architecture is an alternative to conventional, multilayer film fabrication. This process uses less-reactive electrode materials that are easier to manufacture and are more durable and reliable than conventional materials. OLED efficiency is improved by increasing charge injection and using nano-structured materials at the electrode-organic interface. The structured materials are insensitive to air or water and have improved charge balance and a low refractive-index microstructure. These features also improve light out-coupling in the organic light-emitting layer, thereby producing higher OLED efficacy.

A similar process can be applied to LED fabrication, where the micro- and nano-scale heteroepitaxy process reduces structural defects in wide bandgap semiconductor layers. The resulting high-quality crystalline structure provides current confinement, which reduces heat generation and improves efficacy. The structure also forms an internal light-guide, which further improves device efficiency. LBNL is currently seeking potential industrial partners to commercialize the technology.

LBNL's OLED Material and Prototype Sample Display (inset).

Technology History
- Developed by LBNL.
- Seeking potential industrial partners to commercialize the technology.

Applications
Can be used to provide energy-efficient area lighting and information displays.

Capabilities
- Uses a scalable micro- and nanofabrication process to produce structured OLEDs and LEDs.
- Enhances charge injection and light extraction for increased efficacy.
- Improves device performance to levels suitable for widespread deployment.

Benefits

Durability
Increases product lifetime by using low-defect, stable materials.

Performance
Enhances device efficiency by improving electrical and optical output.

Productivity
Uses imprint-based fabrication and vapor deposition steps to simplify the manufacturing process.

Contact Information:
Dr. Samuel S. Mao
Email: SSMao@lbl.gov
Phone: (510) 486-7038
Lawrence Berkeley National Laboratory
1 Cyclotron Rd. MS-701-108B
Berkeley, CA 94720
Website: http://www.lbl.gov

Key Technologies for White Lighting Based on LEDs: Precise Temperature Measurement

Novel Pyrometer Enables Precise Temperature Measurement during Growth of InGaN LEDs

Temperature measurement during indium gallium nitride (InGaN) metalorganic chemical vapor deposition (MOCVD) is very difficult due to the transparency of the substrates (e.g., sapphire) and epilayers at the near-IR wavelengths (e.g., 900-1000 nm) normally used for pyrometry. Until recently, no method has been readily available to measure the true wafer surface temperature during deposition. The problem is particularly severe because the InGaN composition (and therefore emission wavelength) is extremely sensitive to temperatures from 700-800°C. Because of errors in existing temperature measurement techniques, process drifts of 10-20°C are common, leading to InGaN devices that emit light outside of the target wavelength window.

SNL's NUV Pyrometer for TemperatureMeasurement During InGaN LED Growth.

With assistance from the U.S. Department of Energy's Building Technologies Program, Sandia National Laboratories (SNL) is developing a new type of pyrometer to accurately and precisely measure the temperature during the MOCVD process. Unlike existing equipment, this pyrometer was developed based on high-temperature GaN opacity in the near-ultraviolet (NUV) wavelength range of approximately 400 nm. The ability to measure thermal radiation at wavelengths where the wafer and/or epilayer are opaque greatly enhances temperature control, which will increase the yield of InGaN epitaxial material and significantly lower the cost of the final LED products.

SNL is currently collaborating with Veeco Instruments, Inc., to further develop an in-situ pyrometer for accurate substrate temperature measurement. The next-generation NUV pyrometer will measure the wafer temperature distribution with both high-temperature resolution and spatial resolution during growth of the active region of InGaN LEDs.

Technology History
- Developed by SNL.
- Continuing work involves collaboration with Veeco Instruments, Inc., to further develop an in-situ pyrometer that accurately measures substrate temperatures.

Applications
Can be used to improve the temperature control of the MOCVD process during the growth of InGaN LEDs.

Capabilities
- Accurately and precisely measures the GaN/sapphire wafer temperature during the growth of InGaN LEDs.
- Achieves temperature-reporting accuracy to within 1°C.
- Enables narrower emission wavelength range for LEDs.

Benefits

Cost Savings
Reduces the cost of final LED products by increasing the production yield of InGaN epitaxial material.

Product Quality
Produces InGaN devices that emit light within a target wavelength window by eliminating process temperature drifts associated with conventional measurement techniques.

> Contact Information:
> Dr. Robert Biefeld
> *Email:* rmbiefe@sandia.gov
> *Phone:* (505) 844-1556
> Sandia National Laboratories
> PO Box 5800 Albuquerque,
> NM 87185-1086
> Website: http://www.sandia.gov

Nanowire-Templated Lateral Epitaxy of Low-Dislocation-Density GaN

New Technique Enables Inexpensive
Production of High-Quality GaN Substrates

Solid-state lighting (SSL) has the potential to provide light that is much more efficient and longer-lasting than conventional technologies, resulting in significant energy savings and reduced carbon emissions. The basis of most SSL devices is the light-emitting diode (LED), which typically consists of a sandwich of gallium nitride (GaN)-based semiconductor layers. LEDs are typically grown on sapphire substrates because of the lack of bulk GaN crystal. Large lattice mismatch, or difference in atomic spacing, between GaN and the sapphire substrate results in defects forming in the GaN layers. These defects significantly reduce device efficiency and lifetime, hindering the development of higher performance SSL.

With assistance from the U.S. Department of Energy's Building Technologies Program, Sandia National Laboratories (SNL) is developing an innovative and inexpensive GaN crystal growth technique called nanowire-templated lateral epitaxial growth (NTLEG). The process uses aligned arrays of single-crystalline GaN nanowires as templates for the growth of high-quality GaN on sapphire substrates. The single-step process results in lateral GaN film formation that bridges the substrate and the nanowire array. The nanowire's small dimensions (typically <100 nm diameter) provide lateral strain relief and reduce lattice mismatch. The strain relaxation effect reduces defect density by 50 times compared with GaN films grown by conventional multistep techniques. SNL will continue to optimize the process to achieve higher quality GaN films and plans to extend the technique to grow indium gallium nitride (InGaN) and other semiconductors.

Technology History
- Developed by SNL.
- Planning to extend the technique to grow InGaN and other semiconductors.

Applications
Can be used to produce LEDs for SSL devices with a reduced number of defects, which improves device efficiency and durability.

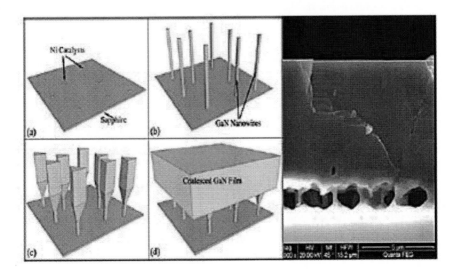

SNL's Nanowire-Templated GaN Film Growth Process.

Capabilities
- Reduces defect density by 50 times compared with conventional sapphire-GaN growth techniques.
- Offers high-quality film growth.
- Can be applied to other types of semiconductor material growth.

Benefits

Cost Savings
Provides a single-step process that reduces costs and complexity compared with other defect reduction methods.

Product Quality
Improves quality, leading to increased device output and lifetime.

Contact Information:
Dr. George T. Wang
Email: gtwang@sandia.gov
Phone: (505) 284-9212
Sandia National Laboratories
PO Box 5800 Albuquerque,
NM 87185-1086
Website: http://www.sandia.gov

Phosphor-Free Solid-State Lighting Sources

New LEDs Generate White Light
without Using Phosphors

Typical white light-emitting diode (LED) sources consist of a blue LED plus a phosphor material, which is used to convert the LED emission wavelength into a broad spectrum, creating white light. Although high-power LEDs have been produced with this technique, problems exist with device lifetime, efficacy, and color temperature. A need exists for solid-state lighting (SSL) devices that can produce high-efficacy white light without the drawbacks of phosphor-based designs.

With assistance from the U.S. Department of Energy's Building Technologies Program, Cermet Inc., is developing a phosphor-free technology that incorporates a blue LED and dopants within a substrate material. The blue LED emissions excite the dopants, which then emit red and green wavelengths to produce white light. This approach addresses several of the limitations present in a typical white LED source. One key advantage comes from integrating the red and green components in the substrate, which provides a more efficient process for photon conversion. In addition, the use of low-defect-density device structures improves the device's optical performance and durability.

Cermet has developed advanced LED prototypes and has demonstrated a device that provides warm white light. Future development will focus on increasing the total lumen output and efficacy of the prototype device. Cermet continues to seek out and explore possible collaboration and investment partnership opportunities as they prepare to release the technology into the marketplace.

Technology History
- Developed by Cermet Inc., with assistance from the Georgia Institute of Technology.
- Focusing on increasing the total lumen output and efficacy of the device.

Applications
Can be used as an alternative to phosphor-based SSL technologies in the general illumination marketplace.

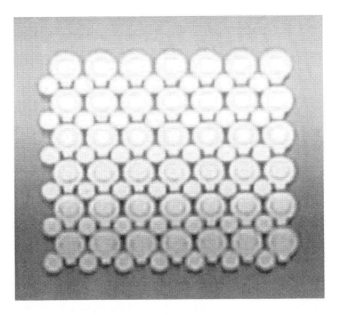

Cermet's Phosphor-Free SSL Technology.

Capabilities
- Produces white light by color mixing emissions from a blue LED with red and green light from within the substrate.
- Enables white LEDs to be fabricated in vertical current geometries.
- Allows white LEDs to be produced without phosphors.

Benefits

Cost Savings
Reduces the cost of fabricating white LEDs by combining the substrate and phosphor functions in a single stage.

Efficiency
Increases white LED efficacy to the levels required for general illumination applications.

Manufacturability
Uses typical commercial approaches for substrate growth and LED epitaxial growth.

> Contact Information:
> Jeff Nause
> *Email:* jnause@cermetinc.com
> *Phone:* (404) 351-0005
> Cermet Inc.
> 1015 Collier Rd, Bldg G Atlanta, GA 30318
> Website: http://www.cermetinc.com

Photoluminescent Nanofibers for High-Efficiency Solid-State Lighting Phosphors

Advanced Nanoscale Materials Enable High-Quality Color Rendering
Polymer nanofibers are nanoscale materials whose properties can be adjusted to manage the lighting performance of high-efficiency solid-state lighting (SSL) luminaires. By controlling fiber diameter, fiber packing, and fiber morphology, a low-cost, high-performance optical material can be fabricated. When used in SSL devices, nanofibers can take the form of either

diffuse reflectors or photoluminescent materials that promote high-efficiency light output and provide color blending to desired chromaticity.

With assistance from the U.S. Department of Energy's Building Technologies Program, Research Triangle Institute (RTI) International is developing advanced nanofiber materials for SSL applications. RTI developed nanofiber reflectors (NFRs) that displayed high diffuse reflectance with reflectance values in excess of 95%. In contrast, traditional reflector materials such as aluminum and paint typically possess reflectance values below 80% and absorb a larger fraction of light, reducing luminaire output efficiency. Incorporating the NFR technology into reflectors, troffers, and beam formers present in SSL luminaires provides better reflectance and lower light loss than is possible with conventional materials.

RTI's photoluminescent nanofibers (PLNs) were formed by combining nanofibers with photoluminescent materials such as phosphors and quantum dots. Forming the PLNs with the proper combination of green and red luminescent materials and exciting the nanocomposite with a blue light-emitting diode were demonstrated to produce high-efficiency (>55 lumens per watt) white light with excellent color rendering properties. Incorporating quantum dots in the PLNs is particularly advantageous because this approach enables any color deficiencies in the light source to be corrected without creating unnecessary radiation in the near-infrared part of the spectrum. Cost models developed during this project have demonstrated that both the NFR and PLN materials can be mass produced at a manufacturing cost that makes them commercially attractive.

High-Quality Color Rendering Provided by an LEDLuminaire Using RTI's PLN and NFR Technology.

Technology History
- Developed by RTI International, in partnership with Dimatix, Inc., Evident Technologies, Donaldson Company, and Elmarco, Inc.
- Tested advanced lighting designs containing photoluminescent nanofibers and nanofiber reflectors.
- Currently seeking to license the technology.

Applications
Can be used to improve the light output quality of phosphor-converted LEDs.

Capabilities
- Achieves a luminous efficacy in excess of 55 lumens per watt and a color rendering index of 90 for both neutral and warm white illumination. Light output is color tunable and diffuse.
- Enables high quantum efficiency down-conversion of LED wavelengths to produce full-spectrum white light.

Benefits

Cost Savings
Enables cost-effective solutions for diffuse, high-reflectance light management across the visible spectrum.

Versatility
Can be conformed to various geometries imposed by light fixtures, thus enabling new lighting designs.

Contact Information:
Lynn Davis
Email: ldavis@rti.org
Phone: (919) 316-3325
Research Triangle Institute
3040 E Cornwallis Rd. Research Triangle Park,
NC 27709
Website: http://www.rti.org/

Efficient Large-Area WOLED Lighting

New Technology Provides Energy-Efficient, Uniform White Lighting over Large Areas

The U.S. Energy Information Administration estimates that approximately 720 TWh of electricity were used for lighting by the U.S. commercial and residential sectors in 2008. This figure represents about 13% of total U.S. electricity consumption. Incandescent and fluorescent lighting, the dominant lighting technologies in use today, suffer from low energy efficiency. Energy-saving, long-lifetime light emitting diodes (LEDs) have experienced some success entering the market for use in traffic lights and large advertisement panels. However, these large panels are costly to assemble because they are made up of many small LED light bulbs. A need exists for an LED technology that can be cost-effectively scaled to provide lighting over large areas.

With the assistance of a U.S. Department of Energy Small Business Innovation Research grant, Universal Display Corporation (UDC) is developing a new type of phosphorescent white organic LED (WOLED) technology for use in large-area illumination applications. UDC's WOLEDs require less energy to produce light than incandescent and most fluorescent lighting technologies and reduce the amount of energy lost to the surrounding environment as heat. UDC deposits the WOLED materials on glass substrates via thermal evaporation, a process that is easily scalable to large-area panels. The panels offer a diffuse source of illumination, eliminating the need for external diffusers such as lamp shades. UDC's WOLED technology also enables transparent window panels, such as skylights, to double as light sources. The panels can be transparent in the "off" state, allowing daylight to pass through. At night, the panels are turned to the "on" state to provide overhead lighting.

UDC is currently making 6" x 6" panels with efficacies exceeding 50 lm/W. The panels can be stacked side-by-side to cover large areas or cut into more intricate patterns for architectural designs. To bring the technology to the marketplace, UDC is partnering with Moser Baer Technologies and Armstrong World Industries, Inc. Moser Baer will manufacture the WOLED panels at a U.S.-based facility, while Armstrong will incorporate the panels into their TechZone™ ceiling systems.

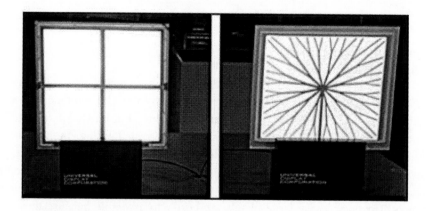

UDC's Phosphorescent WOLED Lighting Panels.

Technology History
- Developed by UDC, in partnership with the University of Michigan and the University of Southern California.
- Currently partnering with Moser Baer Technologies and Armstrong World Industries, Inc.

Applications
Can be used as a high-efficiency replacement for traditional lighting sources (i.e., incandescent, fluorescent, and halogen) used in general illumination applications.

Capabilities
- Produces a uniform white light output over a large area.
- Achieves a luminous efficacy exceeding 50 lm/W.
- Achieves an LT70 lifetime of 10,000 hours at a luminance of 1,000 cd/m^2.

Benefits

Cost Savings
Reduces operating costs relative to conventional lighting sources via energy-efficient operation.

Safety

Uses non-toxic materials in manufacturing without the mercury present in compact fluorescent bulbs.

Versatility

Can be fabricated on a variety of flexible substrate materials, including glass, plastics, and thin stainless steel.

Contact Information:
Mike Hack
Email: mikehack@universaldisplay.com
Phone: (609) 671-0980
Universal Display Corporation
375 Phillips Boulevard Ewing, NJ 08618
Website: http://www.universaldisplay.com/

Highly Efficient OLEDs for General Illumination

New Light-Scattering Substrates
Improve OLED Light Extraction Efficiency

In order for organic light-emitting diodes (OLEDs) to become viable alternatives to conventional lighting sources, their energy efficiency must be improved. Currently, only 20% of the light photons generated in OLEDs are able to escape from the OLED structure and contribute to useful illumination. Major OLED manufacturers typically deposit a light-scattering layer on the external surface of the glass or polymer substrates upon which the OLED devices are fabricated. Because of the very thin (~100 nm) active layers in OLED devices, flat substrates with very small surface roughness are necessary in order to achieve reliable and reproducible device production. This requirement presents a major challenge for fabrication of the light-scattering layer on the same side of the substrate that is used for deposition of the OLED structure.

With the assistance of a U.S. Department of Energy Small Business Innovation Research grant, Physical Optics Corporation demonstrated that fabrication of the light-scattering layer on the inner surface of OLED substrates (i.e., at the interface between the OLED structure and substrate) significantly improves photon extraction efficiency. Physical Optics' technology enables deposition of light-scattering layers with the required surface quality on both rigid (glass) and flexible (polymer) substrates.

The new substrates are compatible with the current OLED manufacturing process used by GE Global Research, a leading OLED technology company. Testing conducted by the Eastman Kodak Company has also confirmed that Physical Optics' substrate technology improves the light extraction efficiency of OLEDs.

Technology History
- Developed by Physical Optics Corporation.
- Received positive testing feedback from major lighting companies regarding substrate performance and manufacturing compatibility.

Applications
Can be used to improve the performance of OLED-based devices used for displays, decorative illumination, and general lighting applications.

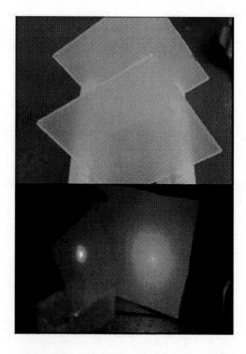

Physical Optics Corporation's Light-ScatteringSubstrates for OLEDs (top) DemonstratingLaser Beam Scattering (bottom).

Capabilities
- Improves OLED light extraction efficiency by 50%.
- Optimizes light scattering for specific OLED devices.
- Can be fabricated on rigid or flexible substrates.

Benefits

Performance
Improves efficiency, light output uniformity, and color rendering of OLEDs.

Productivity
Provides compatibility with established OLED manufacturing techniques, including high-volume roll-to-roll processing.

Contact Information:
Rick Shie
Email: rshie@poc.com
Phone: (310) 320-3088
Physical Optics Corporation
20600 Gramercy Place Torrance, CA 90501-1821
Website: http://www.poc.com/

Low-Cost, High-Efficiency Polymer OLEDs Based on Stable p-i-n Device Architecture

Novel OLED Architecture Enables Low-Cost SSL Print Manufacturing
Organic light-emitting diode (OLED) technology came to international attention with the Kodak OLED work in the 1980s, which showed the potential for this fundamentally new display and lighting technology. Since then, significant developments in OLED efficiency and lifetime have been achieved that can now exceed conventional technologies. However, the manufacturing processes for these OLEDs rely on display and semiconductor industry vacuum-based technology, which has significant throughput and capital cost limitations. A new OLED manufacturing process is needed that can be cost competitive with other lighting approaches.

Add-Vision, Inc. (AVI), with assistance from the U.S. Department of Energy's Building Technologies Program, has pioneered an all-printed structure based on doped polymer active layer materials and printed air-stable cathodes. This development enables the use of high throughput printing with reduced environmental control in the manufacturing process and reduced encapsulation requirements for the finished device. AVI is also working to improve efficiencies by including printable, solution-based phosphorescent emitters and stable p-i-n printed multilayer structuring.

Full, flexible OLED fabrication is also within the scope of this work, including flexible encapsulation and the development of related materials. AVI is scaling this approach to larger device processing (A4) on roll-based tools and producing flexible white emitting prototypes from the all printed fabrication line. This process will also be used in the near term for entry-level product prototyping with development and commercialization partners.

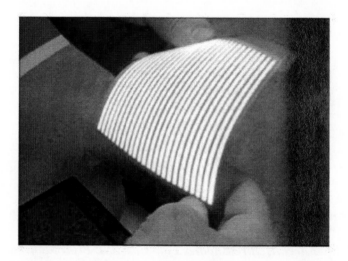

Flexible White OLED Device Printed by Add-Vision, Inc.

Technology History
- Developed by AVI in partnership with the University of California Santa Cruz and the University of California Los Angeles.
- Continuing work on improving color quality and manufacturing throughput and efficiency.

Applications
Can be used to manufacture OLED devices for entry-level solid-state lighting (SSL) applications.

Capabilities
- Produces flexible, white OLED devices using print technology for emitter and cathode materials.
- Enables high-rate manufacturing at speeds of up to 1 m/sec and is scalable to large web widths.

Benefits

Cost Savings
Reduces costs by using high throughput, low capital cost print manufacturing tools on flexible substrates.

Efficiency
Maximizes efficiency of fully printed devices by using solution-based phosphorescent materials and p-i-n doping architectures.

```
Contact Information:
Devin MacKenzie
Email: devinm@add-vision.com
Phone: (518) 276-3755
Add-Vision, Inc.
1600 Green Hills Road, Suite 100 Scotts Valley,
CA 95066
Website: http://www.add-vision.com/
```

OLEDs for General Lighting

Novel Technology Saves Energy and Enables
New Product Configurations for Lighting
Lighting represents a large fraction of energy use in residential and commercial buildings. Any technological improvement that increases lighting efficiency and is adopted by large numbers of consumers will substantially reduce buildings' energy consumption. Conventional light sources, such as those based on incandescent and fluorescent technologies, are mature and

therefore unlikely to experience dramatic increases in efficiency. Semiconductor-based light-emitting diodes (LEDs) have enabled significant energy-efficiency gains in lighting applications but are still primarily limited to use in rigid fixtures and surfaces. LEDs are also concentrated sources of light and therefore require a diffuser for use in most indoor lighting applications. A need exists for an energy-efficient lighting source that provides diffuse lighting in a variety of product configurations.

With assistance from the U.S. Department of Energy's Building Technologies Program, GE Global Research is developing organic light-emitting diode (OLED) technology that will provide energy-efficient, diffuse light that can be tailored to a number of different product configurations. The organic semiconductors in OLEDs are amorphous, so they can be deposited on flexible substrates via low-cost techniques such as printing. Many lighting applications can take advantage of this flexibility, such as roll-up portable displays or large-area displays requiring curved surfaces. In addition, OLEDs are now being seriously considered for space lighting applications. GE's OLED technology is now four times more energy efficient than incandescent bulbs. OLEDs can also be installed directly into ceilings or walls without the need for external diffusers like lampshades. To accelerate the penetration of OLED technology into both the display and space lighting markets, GE continues to work on improving device performance and developing a high-volume, roll-to-roll manufacturing process.

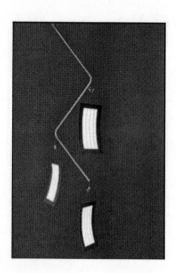

GE's Flexible OLEDs.

Technology History

- Developed by GE Global Research, beginning in 2000.
- Currently developing a roll-to-roll approach for OLED fabrication to enable low-cost production of flexible lighting products.

Applications

Can be used in general lighting applications, especially wherever diffuse illumination and/or flexible lighting devices are required.

Capabilities

- Produces high-quality diffuse light.
- Achieves a luminous efficacy four times greater than incandescent lighting.

Benefits

Cost Savings

Reduces costs by using high-volume, rollto-roll manufacturing.

Design Flexibility

Enables lighting integration with curved or bendable surfaces in ways that are not possible for traditional lighting sources.

Versatility

Can be deposited on a variety of flexible substrates such as plastic, glass, and thin metal foil.

Contact Information:
Anil Duggal
Email: duggal@ge.com
Phone: (518) 387-7424
GE Global Research
1 Research Circle Niskayuna,
NY 12309
Website: http://ge.geglobalresearch.com/

Transparent Conducting Oxides and Undercoat Technologies for Economical OLED Lighting

Alternative Material Reduces Cost of OLED Production

Organic light-emitting diode (OLED) devices require at least one transparent conducting layer as an electrode to carry electrical charge(s) while allowing light to pass through. Current commercial OLED devices use indium tin oxide (ITO) for the transparent conducting oxide (TCO) layer. Indium metal is relatively rare and expensive and is used predominately for optoelectronic applications such as flat panel displays. However, indium's high price and limited supply tend to make indium-based OLEDs expensive and will limit the market penetration of this energy-efficient technology. Recently, TCOs based on zinc oxide have shown promise as an economical alternative to ITO. Compared with indium, zinc is more abundant in nature and is used in a variety of applications, resulting in a stable supply and lower production costs.

OLED Devices Containing DopedZnO on a 6"x 6" Glass Substrate.

Arkema Inc. and Philips Lighting, with assistance from the U.S. Department of Energy's Building Technologies Program, are developing a process whereby a zinc-based TCO layer is deposited onto flat glass using atmospheric pressure chemical vapor deposition (APCVD). APCVD technology is similar to what has been used for the last 20+ years to make low-emissivity windows with fluorine doped tin oxide (FTO). The glass moves through the process very quickly, allowing only a few seconds for the deposition of precursors to form the TCO. The APCVD process also allows for excellent homogeneity across a glass ribbon (typically 3 meters) while achieving desired TCO electrical requirements and optical properties. Meeting these expectations by APCVD enables the potential production of millions of square meters of coated glass per float line at a reasonable cost.

The current project focuses on using APCVD to deposit doped ZnO TCO. The process advantages are similar to FTO, but the optoelectronic properties are superior to FTO and similar to the standard set by ITO in this market.

Technology History
- Developed by Arkema Inc. and Philips Lighting.
- Focusing on scaling up OLED device fabrication and the producing precursors.

Applications
Can be used as a TCO alternative to ITO for OLEDs or other devices that utilize ITO.

Capabilities
- Achieves >90% transmission in the visible spectrum.
- Offers electrical and thickness specifications equivalent to commercially available ITO.
- Offers comparable optical performance to commercially available ITO.

Benefits

Cost Savings
Provides an alternative, cost-effective raw material for OLED TCO layers.

Manufacturability
Processes easily and is highly adaptable to large-volume production.

Product Quality
Improves substrate adhesion compared with commercially available ITO.

Contact Information:
Jason Pomanteary
Email: jason.pomante@arkema.com
Phone: (215) 419-5407
Arkema Inc.
2000 Market Street Philadelphia,
PA 19103
Website: http://www.arkema-inc.com

Transparent Conductive Oxides for OLEDs

Indium-Free Flexible Substrate Reduces OLED Manufacturing Costs

Organic light-emitting diodes (OLEDs) have the potential to reduce lighting energy consumption and provide designers with options for unique lighting applications. The transparent conductive oxide (TCO) layer, an electrode that enables current flow through the device while allowing visible light to pass through, is a key component of all OLEDs. The majority of TCOs currently contain indium, which is very expensive due to its scarcity and the high demand for its use in liquid crystal displays and touchscreen devices. An alternative TCO material is needed that will reduce the costs associated with OLED manufacturing and enable the widespread adoption of OLED lighting.

With assistance from the U.S. Department of Energy's Building Technologies Program, Pacific Northwest National Laboratory (PNNL) and the National Renewable Energy Laboratory (NREL) are developing a flexible OLED substrate technology that eliminates the cost and availability barriers associated with indium and can be manufactured on a large scale. The technology uses a sputtering technique capable of depositing an indium-free TCO (gallium-doped zinc oxide) uniformly over a large area. The process is performed at lower temperatures and allows for the use of flexible plastic substrates. Blue phosphorescent OLED devices fabricated using this method demonstrate excellent operating voltage (<4V) and efficacy (>35 lm/W) at a luminance of 800 Cd/m^2. General lighting applications typically would require approximately 5,000 Cd/m^2 at 4.9 V and 26 lm/W.

The new technology could serve as an inexpensive, flexible substrate for manufacturing large-scale OLED devices. Producing OLEDs on flexible substrates for mass production through high-volume processes such as roll-to-roll manufacturing could enable applications in general lighting, decorative lighting, displays, and solar panels.

PNNL's High-Efficiency Blue OLED.

Technology History
- Developed by PNNL's lighting team and NREL's TCO team.
- Preparing to scale up for commercialization; seeking partner(s) for high-volume manufacturing.

Applications
Can be used for large-area displays, general lighting, decorative lighting, and photovoltaics on flexible substrates.

Capabilities
- Produces flexible electrode substrates.
- Provides an alternative to rigid, indiumtin-oxide based electrodes.
- Enables high-efficiency OLED technology that achieves 39 lm/W at 1 mA/cm^2.

Benefits

Cost Savings
Reduces costs by replacing indium with more abundant materials.

Energy Savings

Reduces energy consumed for lighting applications by increasing OLED efficiency.

Manufacturability

Enables high-volume manufacturing on flexible substrates.

Contact Information: Dr. Daniel Gaspar *Email:* daniel.gaspar@pnl.gov *Phone:* (509) 375-2544 Pacific Northwest National Laboratory PO Box 999, 902 Battelle Blvd. Richland, WA 99352 Website: http://www.pnl.gov

Advanced Coatings to Improve the Efficiency, Color Rendering, and Life of High-Intensity-Discharge Lamps

Advanced Coating Significantly Increases Efficiency of HID Lamps

High-intensity-discharge (HID) lamps are used extensively for large area lighting such as parking lots, streets, and warehouses and are increasingly used for general lighting in stores and homes. HID lamps account for 26% of the lighting energy used in the United States, or about 200 TWh. Based on present HID use, a 20% increase in the efficacy of HID lamps would result in a significant U.S. energy savings of 40 TWh per year.

With assistance from a U.S. Department of Energy Small Business Innovation Research grant, Acree Technologies Inc. is developing an inexpensive, robust, single-layer coating that is applied to the outside of an HID lamp. The coating reflects infrared (IR) and ultraviolet (UV) photons back into the lamp, heating the plasma and increasing the lumen output for a given electrical energy input. Measurements demonstrate up to a 22% increase in the efficacy (lumens/watt) between coated and uncoated HID lamps, along with improved color rendering.

This optically selective transmissive coating is unique in that it is a single-layer coating that reflects IR and UV and is less expensive than previous multilayer coatings. The coating developed in this project can be applied for pennies per bulb, and the deposition process is compatible with large-scale production. The thickness of the coating is not critical, making the coating easy to produce. In addition, the coating is robust and lasts throughout the lifetime of the bulb.

Technology History
- Developed by Acree Technologies Inc.
- Partnering with Venture Lighting, a major HID lamp manufacturer.
- Currently testing coatings and anticipating that end user testing will begin in the next several months.

Applications
Can be used on any HID lamp to significantly improve the lamp's efficiency and color rendering.

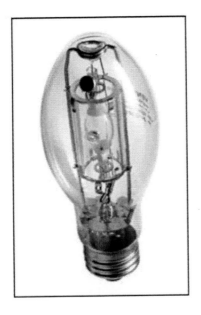

HID Lamp with Acree's OpticallySelective Transmissive Coating.

Capabilities
- Increases lamp efficacy over 20% compared with uncoated lamps.
- Offers a simple, inexpensive and adaptable process for retrofitting most HID lamps.
- Provides compatibility with existing manufacturing processes.

Benefits

Cost Savings
Improves lamp efficacy, significantly reducing lighting cost and energy consumption.

Durability
Provides a robust coating that lasts throughout the lifetime of the HID lamp.

Product Quality
Improves light output and the color rendering index of the lamp.

Contact Information:
Mike McFarland
Email: mcfarland@acreetech.com
Phone: (925) 798-5770
Acree Technologies Inc.
1980 Olivera Rd., Suite D Concord,
CA 94520
Website: http://www.acreetech.com

Optical Fiber Polymer Processing Techniques for Distributed Lighting

New Manufacturing Process for Optical
Fibers Reduces Cost of Distributed Lighting Systems
The primary hurdle for introducing an energy-efficient accent lighting alternative to incandescent and halogen-based systems is achieving proper light quality at a competitive first cost. Compact fluorescent lamps have low brightness and cannot form a high-intensity beam. Metal halide lamps cannot be scaled to low wattages, and the cost of one lamp and ballast per light point is prohibitive. Traditional accent lighting systems route electrical conduit and wiring to multiple light fixtures within a room. A distributed lighting system is needed that can reduce costs by using one lamp and ballast for multiple points of light.

With the assistance of a U.S. Department of Energy Small Business Innovation Research grant, Energy Focus, Inc., is developing a new distributed lighting system that uses efficient, large core plastic optical fibers (LCPOFs) to direct light from one lamp and ballast to 8 independent spots of accent lighting. The ability to provide lighting for multiple spots reduces the cost per spot of metal halide lamps to that of halogen-based systems. Fiber optic accent lighting systems also require far fewer electrical service connection points than traditional systems. The Energy Focus system saves energy by using 99.5% of the light produced and generating less heat than systems with multiple incandescent or halogen bulbs. In addition, fiber optic distributed lighting reduces maintenance costs compared with traditional systems because the number of bulb replacements is reduced.

LCPOFs have historically accounted for nearly 50% of fiber optic accent lighting system costs. Energy Focus developed new LCPOF processing techniques that significantly reduce the post-extrusion processing time of the cable's polymer core and thereby reduce manufacturing costs. In addition, the amount of fluorinated ethylene-propylene (FEP) cladding was minimized without detrimentally effecting light attenuation and color shift. These cost-reducing features will help enable large-scale adoption of this technology.

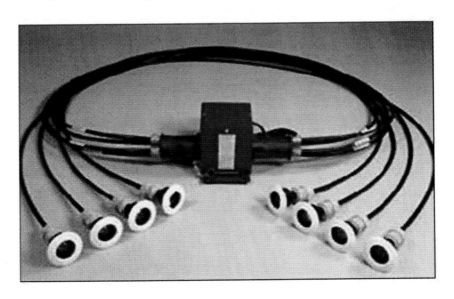

Energy Focus' LCPOFs in a Distributed Lighting System.

Technology History
- Developed by Energy Focus, Inc.
- Developing a cost-effective, high-intensity discharge lamp distributed lighting system using LCPOF technology.

Applications
Can be used to provide a cost-competitive accent lighting alternative to traditional incandescent and halogen-based systems.

Capabilities
- Provides energy-efficient distributed accent lighting with instant-on capability.
- Reduces fiber optic cable manufacturing costs by up to 90% and shortens polymer core post-extrusion processing time.

Benefits

Cost Savings
Reduces the manufacturing cost of LCPOF cables and the cost of bulb replacements compared with traditional systems.

Energy Savings
Delivers 99.5% of the light produced by the lamp and generates less waste heat than incandescent and halogen systems.

Simplicity
Offers simple installation requiring fewer electrical connections than traditional accent lighting systems with multiple light fixtures.

Contact Information:
Roger Buelow
Email: rbuelow@efoi.com
Phone: (440) 715-1251
Energy Focus, Inc.
32000 Aurora Road Solon,
OH 44139
Website: http://www.energyfocusinc.com

Selective, Emitter-Based, Energy-Efficient Incandescent Lamp Technology

New Ceramic Coating Improves Incandescent Lamp Performance

Currently available commercial incandescent lamps are popular because of their desirable traits, such as low cost, ability to dim, and favorable color rendition. As a result, over 2.75 billion incandescent lamps are produced each year to fill more than 2 billion lighting sockets in the U.S. residential market. However, current incandescent lamp products have low energy efficiency and a relatively short life expectancy. In addition, currently available lighting products with improved energy efficiency are significantly more expensive than the incandescent lamps they replace and/or do not effectively operate in the standard incandescent lamp sockets. A new lamp type is needed that has the appearance and aesthetic lighting qualities of common incandescent lamps, significantly higher energy efficiency, and a price that is close to regular incandescent products. Such a product would be highly desirable from an energy-saving standpoint and would satisfy the demands of consumers.

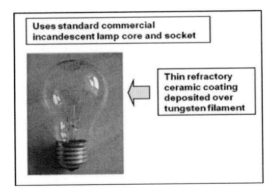

Incandescent Lamp Filament with Surmet Corporation's Ceramic Coating.

With the assistance of a U.S. Department of Energy Small Business Innovation Research grant, Surmet Corporation is developing a novel ceramic coating for incandescent lamp filaments that will increase lamp efficiency and life expectancy. The refractory ceramic coating reduces emission in the infrared part of the spectrum, thereby increasing lamp efficacy. Surmet has designed the processes for coating application to be easily integrated into existing high-volume incandescent lamp production lines. Surmet is building equipment to measure lamp efficacy and conducting lamp testing for extended periods of time. Results will be provided to Surmet's lamp manufacturing partner for assessment as the next step towards commercialization.

Technology History
- Developed by Surmet Corporation in partnership with a major incandescent lamp manufacturer.
- Currently conducting efficacy tests for incandescent lamps using the filament.

Applications
Can be used to increase the energy efficiency and extend the life expectancy of incandescent lamps.

Capabilities
- Increases incandescent lamp efficacy to 30 lumens per watt (LPW) compared with 15 LPW for currently available lamps.
- Extends incandescent lamp life expectancy to 2,000 hours.
- Maintains aesthetic lighting qualities of current incandescent lamps, such as a color rendering index >97 at a correlated color temperature of approximately 3000 K.

Benefits

Cost Savings
Achieves large efficiency improvement over current incandescent lamps without the excessive cost penalty associated with halogen and compact fluorescent lamps.

Productivity
Integrates easily into existing high-volume incandescent lamp production lines.

Contact Information:
Uday Kashalikar
Email: ukashalikar@surmet.com
Phone: (781) 345-5727
Surmet Corporation
31 B Street Burlington, MA 01803
Website: http://www.surmet.com

Adaptive Liquid Crystal Windows

New Window Glazing Technology Reduces HVAC Energy Consumption

Almost 30% of the energy used to heat and cool U.S. homes (2.7 quads annually) is lost through windows. Currently, energy conservation is a top national priority given the desire to reduce oil consumption and greenhouse gas emissions. A major contribution to energy conservation could be made by eliminating HVAC energy consumption from solar loading, especially during the warm summer months. Various reflective window technologies have been developed to reduce summer cooling loads, but these technologies do not provide any benefit during the winter.

With assistance from the U.S. Department of Energy's Building Technologies program, AlphaMicron, Inc., is developing an active window glazing technology that adapts to seasonal climate change and reduces year round energy consumption. The adaptive windows reduce the amount of solar loading by controlling the amount of sunlight transmitted through the window, less in the summer and more in the winter. An additional benefit of this technology is that the light transmission is controlled without creating an unpleasant interior environment, e.g., excessive glare or darkness. Interior décor is also protected from ultraviolet and solar heating damage.

AlphaMicron's adaptive, smart window film technology consists of liquid crystal deposited on a flexible substrate instead of glass. The company is developing a unique manufacturing system that uses a roll-to-roll manufacturing process to produce a 14-inch-wide liquid crystal film. Successful commercialization of the technology will require wider films to accommodate most window sizes. AlphaMicron will therefore scale up their manufacturing capabilities to produce 48-inch-wide smart window films.

AlphaMicron's Adaptive Liquid Crystal Window Technology.

Technology History
- Developed by AlphaMicron, Inc.
- Continuing development of a roll-toroll manufacturing process to produce window films that are 48 inches wide.

Applications
Can be used as an energy-efficient replacement for conventional windows in residential and commercial buildings.

Capabilities
- Offers variable transmission: 70% in winter mode and 30% in summer mode.
- Reduces HVAC energy consumption by manipulating solar loading.

Benefits

Comfort
Controls light transmission to ensure a comfortable living/working space without excessive glare or darkness.

Emissions Reductions
Reduces greenhouse gas emissions by lowering building energy consumption.

Energy Savings
Reduces energy loss through windows and enables energy-efficient buildings.

Versatility
Adapts to residential and commercial applications.

Contact Information:
Bahman Taheri
Email: bahman@alphamicron.com
Phone: (330) 676-0648
AlphaMicron, Inc.
1950 State Route 59 Kent,
OH 44240
Website: http://www.alphamicron.com/

Advanced Framing System with Low-Emissivity Paintfor Commercial Windows

Novel Insulating Window Frame System
Reduces Building Heating and Cooling Loads

Aluminum window framing systems are used in more than 80% of commercial buildings because of their inherently good structural properties and long service lifetime. Unfortunately, traditional window frames suffer from poor insulating performance, making windows one of the least effective parts of a building's envelope. A cost-effective method for improving the insulating capability of commercial-grade aluminum window frames is needed.

With assistance from the U.S. Department of Energy's (DOE's) Building Technologies Program, the Three Rivers Aluminum Company (TRACO) is developing a novel window framing system that will increase the insulative ability of windows in commercial buildings. Heat transfer through window frames occurs through three mechanisms: convection (from air movement), conduction (through the solid parts of frame), and radiation (between frame surfaces and the surrounding environment and/or different surfaces inside the frame cavity). TRACO developed a low-emissivity frame coating, an advanced thermal break system, and a foam-filling (or cavity interruption) technology to reduce radiation, conduction, and convection heat transfer, respectively. The combination of these three technologies into a unified system will improve the U-factor of commercial-grade aluminum window frames by more than 30% compared with traditional window systems using the same glazing.

TRACO has commercialized the individual components of the system on a small-scale basis and is currently working to develop a method for cost-effective, large-scale application of all three technologies in commercial windows. One particular focus of the ongoing research involves developing an aesthetically acceptable white color for the low-emissivity coating. To demonstrate the performance advantages offered by this framing system, windows with the three insulative technologies were installed in a conference room of the DOE's Forrestal Building in 2009.

Technology History
- Developed by TRACO, with assistance from multiple project partners.

- Commercialized individual constituent technologies on a small-scale basis.
- Currently working to develop and commercialize the entire system for large-scale applications.

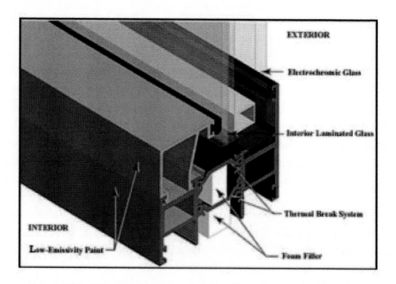

Cross-Section of TRACO's Advanced Commercial Window Framing System.

Applications

Can be used as an energy-saving replacement for conventional aluminum window frames in commercial buildings.

Capabilities

- Improves the U-factor of commercial-grade aluminum window frames by more than 30% compared with traditional window systems using the same glazing.
- Reduces the emissivity value of the interior window frame surface from 0.90 to 0.65.

Benefits

Cost Savings

Reduces heating and air conditioning costs by inhibiting heat transfer through aluminum window frames.

Emissions Reductions

Reduces greenhouse gas emissions by decreasing energy consumption for heating and cooling buildings.

Simplicity

Applies to existing framing systems without any additional modifications.

```
Contact Information:
Sneh Kumar
Email: sneh.kumar@traco.com
Phone: (724) 742-1919
Three Rivers Aluminum Company
171 Progress Avenue Cranberry Township,
PA 16066
Website: http://www.traco.com/
```

Vacuum Glazing Development

Novel Design Improves Durability and Insulating Performance of Windows

Conventional insulating glass units (IGUs) in windows have a typical lifetime of 10 to 20 years, after which seal failure and/or contamination of the internal airspace occurs. Once the seal has failed, a window's insulating performance is drastically reduced. The insulating capability of air-or-gas-filled IGUs is also limited, with double-pane IGUs achieving an insulating value of about R-3.5 and triple-pane IGUs reaching about R-5.5. Currently available vacuum insulating glass units (VIGUs) save more energy but do not last long enough to achieve a full payback of their higher initial cost. A need exists for a VIGU that will offer energy-saving insulative properties over a long lifetime.

With assistance from the U.S. Department of Energy's (DOE's) Building Technologies Program, EverSealed Windows, Inc. (ESW), is developing a new sealing technology that will allow window manufacturers to produce long-lasting VIGUs with exceptional insulating values. The design employs a flexible metal edge seal that is gas-tight and allows the individual panes of a VIGU to expand/contract independently in response to differing inside and outside temperatures. The seal itself, which expands and contracts like an accordion, reduces stress on the window and extends window lifetime. ESW's proprietary glass-to-metal bond has demonstrated the sealing performance necessary for maintaining high-vacuum pressures between the glass panes. The durability of the seal will be verified by performing accelerated thermal cycling tests equivalent to 40 years of use in the field. The panes of glass themselves are kept apart by a system of nearly invisible standoffs.

ESW's VIGU is being designed to withstand the stresses of extreme-temperature environments for at least 25 years, while achieving an insulating value of R-14 or greater. This improved performance will enable a whole-window insulating value of R-10, a long-term DOE goal for helping to achieve cost-effective energy-efficient buildings. The insulating advantage of the VIGU also allows for building designs that incorporate more windows without increasing energy consumption. An increased number of windows allow a greater portion of a building to be lit with natural daylight, resulting in a more comfortable living/working space for the building's occupants.

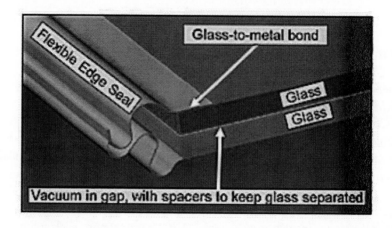

ESW's Durable, Energy-Saving VIGU.

Technology History
- Developed by ESW, with contributions from multiple national laboratories and leading North American window manufacturers.
- Currently testing and demonstrating various durability characteristics of the glass-to-metal bond under extremely hot and cold conditions.

Applications
Can be used wherever highly insulative glass windows and doors are needed, including extreme-temperature climates, sun-facing walls, refrigerated supermarket display units, and vending machine doors.

Capabilities
- Achieves an insulating value of R-14 or greater, enabling a whole-window R-value of R-10.
- Increases windows' high-performance insulating lifetime to 25 years or more.

Benefits

Durability
Increases window lifetime by using a hermetically bonded flexible seal.

Energy Savings
Reduces energy loss through windows, thereby lowering energy consumption for heating and cooling buildings.

Safety
Uses tempered (heat-strengthened) glass in standard units and laminated safety glass when hurricane-resistant windows are required by city or county building codes.

Contact Information:

David Stark

Email: David@EverSealedWindows.com

Phone: (303) 674-1197

EverSealed Windows, Inc.

1999 Interlocken Drive Evergreen,

CO 80439-8952

Website: http://www.eversealedwindows.com/

INDEX

D

T